MW00627503

First Printing, September, 2021

© **2019 TXu002167489**

All rights reserved. No part of this book may be reproduced or transmitted in any form including photocopying, recording, digital imaging, or by any other storage and retrieval system without written permission from the author.

ISBN: 978-1-7343178-0-0

Cover and artwork by Eugene Chugunov (Wickard) of 99 Designs.

Contact Information:
Whimsytreetales@gmail.com

Book One of the Whimsy Tree Tales

Dedication

In loving memory of my dad,

Jack Warren Baker, M.D.,

who taught me how to think and reason,

and how to put pen to paper.

Δ Δ Δ

In loving memory of my mom,

Patricia Gray Baker,

who taught me how to laugh and have fun,

and who brought music and theater into our home.

And to them both for always encouraging my sense of whimsy!

Book One of the Whimsy Tree Tales

Contents

PART 1 — MISSING..................................1

    Then 2

    Now 6

    May's Best 22

    Looking for Answers 57

PART 2 — REMEMBERING 91

    Bad News Bear...................................92

    Edward Edwards............................ 117

    Moving Day 128

    Bacon and Eggs 141

    Miffed with Marlee........................... 162

PART 3 — FINDING 183

    Wing Snatcher Bait 184

    Pointers' Peak................................. 193

    Home Alone.................................... 229

    Waiting Is...................................... 251

ODDS AND ENDS................................271

    Excerpt from Book 2..........................271

    Author's Note 276

    In Appreciation.................................276

Book One of the Whimsy Tree Tales

Book One of the Whimsy Tree Tales

PART 1 — MISSING

There are all kinds of missings: Some come from being alone, others come from the losing of someone or something dear to you, and still others come from some place deep within you that is hard to identify.

This old house has seen better days. It is sad and alone, grieving its missing family.

THEN

The Crossing

Laird MacKenzie was just as cold and hungry as his younger siblings, but he wouldn't let them know. It was difficult enough to keep his own fears at bay, so he told them that the dolphins had been singing to them these last few nights. He said he could hear their voices under the ship even through the pounding of the waves and the creaking of the old boat's bones.

The three of them shared cramped quarters. Laird's bunk was next to their one porthole and served as their only source of natural light. The twins, Emilie and Jack, slept in the bunks on the opposite side of the cabin. The bunk below Laird's was intended to be their play area for card and dice games, but with the heaving swells they'd all been too seasick.

This bunk was used mostly by their mother, the Lady Margaret, when their father was at the helm above. She would lay with them and tell them stories of the new home they were going to across the sea, an enchanted place named Waterford the Brave.

"But why is it named thus?" asked Laird at the beginning of their journey.

"Because the house willingly gave up its life as a whimsy tree to travel to the new world and become a home for your uncle, my dear brother Jon," she replied. Then she'd tell them more stories—not only of Waterford, but also of their old home, Waterglenn the Defender.

Then Emilie asked, "Mother, why did we have to leave Waterglenn?"

"Queen Arian said we must go, and in haste, lest we become victims of your wicked cousin Lord Sebastian's madness. Now enough of this," she said as she tucked each one in tighter against the cold. "We can't change the past. Besides, we have a wonderful new home awaiting us."

Δ Δ Δ

While his family conversed below deck, the Lord Robert MacKenzie drew his red wool scarf more tightly around his neck as he steadied the wheel of the old trawler. She'd been a good ship and served his family well for generations, but this crossing was costing her and them dearly. They had to reach land, and soon, as the last north-easter they'd sailed through had hit her pretty hard.

Letty—or Leticia, as she was properly named—had been built in his grandfather's time. As a boy, he had crewed on her and helped maintain her until the day he finally knew enough to captain her himself.

On this voyage, there had been no time to properly provision Letty before sailing. They'd fled for their lives with few supplies. Something had gone frightfully wrong, and his Maggie told him they must leave and do so quickly, or become the target of an unjust war they had played no hand in creating. Lord MacKenzie mourned the loss of his homeland, and vowed to himself that one day he would avenge this injustice.

While thinking of better times and younger days, the cold wind slipped under his scarf and down his neck once more. Silently he cursed the bitter freeze while praying to the heavens for some relief for himself, his crew, and his family below deck. The children had not been allowed up for days; they were cold and tired, and sick of eating dry, days'-old biscuits and tough meat. In weather like this, even lighting an oil lamp was dangerous.

To Lord MacKenzie's relief, a sailor from Letty's bow finally yelled, "Fair weather ahead, sire."

Upon hearing those welcome words, Lord MacKenzie looked up beyond the wheel housing and thanked God for the forthcoming reprieve from the cold. Within the hour, the seas lessened their mighty swells, the wind her biting curse, and the sun shone down once more upon old Letty's worn and smooth wooden decks.

A cheer came up from all hands as Robert's wife Maggie poked her head out from the cabin door and smiled at him. "Robert, are we through the worst of it, then?" she asked with hope.

"Aye lass, I think we are. I can see our guides, the dolphins, up ahead. We couldn't have crossed these waters without their help."

Three heads bobbed up behind Maggie as their children smiled and asked if they could come up on deck as well. "Aye!" proclaimed their father as he turned the wheel over to his first mate and walked toward his family with loving arms extended, embracing them all. Huddled together, they rejoiced in each other's company.

Anxious to reach their new home, Lord MacKenzie gave his crew orders for completing their journey and finally reaching the port town of Waters End.

Now

House-Hunting

Carson MacKenzie gazed out the window, barely seeing the passing houses as he listened to his own music. He was trying to tune out his parents' voices in the front seat. Texting a friend from their old hometown, he couldn't watch the scenery and type at the same time. Besides, house-hunting was boring. At thirteen, being stuck in a car all day with his eleven-year-old twin siblings—Evan and Marlee—was no fun.

They'd been looking for a new home for a week now, and their father never approved of their choices, so today he was driving them around to see the houses he wanted to check out. It all seemed so ridiculous, as they'd seen some great houses with fantastic yards—huge climbing trees, lots of space to play tag-football in. One even had a swimming pool. Their dad hadn't liked any of these, so still they were searching for a new home.

Turning towards Evan, he saw him holding his nose. Then sniffing himself, he realized what the sour smell he'd been ignoring for the last few moments was. He too held his nose as he looked over to see Marlee on Evan's other side doing the same as she pressed the window button repeatedly and to no effect.

Marlee pointed towards the seat in front of her where their dad sat driving then she gagged. In turn, Evan made a retching sound. Laughing, Carson reached for his window button to confirm it was locked then he kicked the back of his mom's seat.

As their mother Robyn turned around, she saw her children holding their noses and pretended to put her finger down her throat. Then a long drawn out ripping sound echoed through their small space causing them to double-up in laughter.

Oblivious to the antics of his family, their dad continued driving looking neither left nor right except as the pace of traffic, which was very little in this new town, required.

Within a few moments, a rather loud fog horn burped forth followed by a few rather short toots, and by then Robyn had had enough.

"Nelson!" she commanded, "If you must ask for extra peppers and sausage with your cheese omelet, the least you can do is turn off the window lock. We're dying in here," she choked with a grimace.

"What?" he replied rather absently followed quickly by "Oh--sorry. I must have clicked it by mistake."

As three windows slid down at once he explained, "I was thinking about how to handle the Wilson project at work. I didn't even notice," he said half-smiling, embarrassment clear on his face.

Gulping in the fresh air, Carson said, "Good one dad. You almost killed us that time."

As Carson was about to continue teasing, his mom's voice overrode his own.

"Oh, Nelson!" said their mother, Robyn. "Stop the car in front of this house, please."

Pulling over to the side of the road, their father turned to see which house had caught his wife's eye. What he saw was an old, run-down home set well back from the curb, with several broken second-story windows and a wide front porch. The deep yard appeared quite overgrown, increasing his displeasure.

"We've been down this road several times in the last week, and that house is not for sale," Nelson said. "Do you see a sign out front?"

"No dear, but there's something about it that I can't put my finger on. I feel like we belong here, and you can fix it up. It just needs a little love and attention."

"I've already told you that we're looking for a more modern home," Nelson said. "One that's been remodeled with new plumbing, new windows and doors, and has had the electrical circuits replaced. Now let's look at that house down the block, the one that recently posted a For Sale sign out front."

"Oh, but the children and I drove by that one yesterday. It seemed so cold from the outside. It had no character, no charm."

From the back seat, Evan unexpectedly sang forth, "No charm, alarm, alarm! No charm, wiggly-woggly! No charm, gobilly-gookilly!" He proceeded to dance by twisting and turning and pointing to them all from his seat.

Their father smirked at Evan in the rearview mirror. "What was that—a new language, kiddo?"

"Uh, nope," Evan replied, and went still for a moment—which, sitting in the middle rear seat, wasn't easy for him to do.

Carson smiled, thinking about how ridiculous his kid brother could be but secretly enjoying his silliness. The three of them were very close when they weren't fighting over something, and he realized that they had been doing that a lot these days. It must be this new town and not having a home yet or friends to hang out with. Yes, he wanted to live in a house again and was also anxious about who he would meet when school started. Making new friends was not easy for him.

Marlee distracted him from his thoughts by kicking Evan in the shin with her new pointed-toe shoes.

"Ow!" Evan cried, pinching her in retaliation.

Marlee screamed, "Evan just pinched me! He pinched me hard, and I didn't do anything to him!" she lied with just enough strength to be believable.

Nelson threw his hands up in the air. "That's it—I'm done for today! We're going back to the hotel."

"Honey, I'm tired of living in that hotel and eating hotel food every day," Robyn protested, then sighed; she too was weary of house-hunting.

"This is a new job and a new life for all of us," Nelson explained. "I have much more responsibility now. Tomorrow you and the kids can go house-hunting without me. I just don't have time for fighting in the car and looking at inappropriate houses."

Nelson turned to his children in the rear seat. "If your mother has trouble figuring out which house will suit us, each of you has been through the drill. Now I expect you to help her choose wisely tomorrow, understood?"

Like robots, all three nodded at once. Except for Evan, who nodded up and down, then left to right, then up and down again, doing his best not to laugh at his father's seriousness.

Sighing, their dad turned the car around to head back to their hotel—only to glimpse a large object whooshing down in front of him and forcing him to slam on the breaks.

Out of nowhere, a huge tree limb crashed directly in their path, missing their front bumper by inches. It landed with such force that it bounced their car even more than when their dad had slammed on the brakes.

"What the..." he exclaimed. "How the—?"

As the dust began to settle, Robyn craned her neck out the window, looking for the tree the limb must have fallen from. "Where did that come from?" she asked, a bit shaken.

Carson spotted it first. "Wow! Look up there, Mom. It came down from that humongous tree in front of the old house you like."

Glad his family was safe but irritated with the delay, their dad said, "Carson, do something productive with your birthday gift and call 911. Someone has to remove this branch. It spans the whole friggin' width of the road."

Some birthday, Carson thought as he placed the call. The phone was more like a guilt gift, as their father was always away on business these days. He'd only come to one of Carson's Little League games last year, and even missed his graduation at the beginning of summer.

Standing on the walkway of the old house, Carson ignored them all. With a scowl on his face, he brooded and stared at the house with the broken windows. "I'd rather have my old dad back than this darn phone any day," he mumbled. "He's got no time for us, only business. He's changed ever since his last promotion."

Deep in thought, a chill ran down Carson's spine. He sensed he was being watched, and not by his family. He heard a sigh and a soft rumbling, and the ground under his feet swayed ever so slightly.

A little unnerved, Carson looked up at the tree, thinking another branch might be about to fall. He was about to warn his family when his father said, "Let's go!"

Turning, Carson was surprised to see the fallen branch already moved enough to allow one lane in and out. Wondering where the strange sound had come from, he shook his head, thinking it must have been his imagination.

Δ Δ Δ

By dinnertime, Carson looked around the table; nothing seemed to be getting any better. Marlee didn't want cheese on her hamburger, and it came with cheese even though she had said quite clearly, "No cheese, please!" It was melted onto it, and she scraped it off so she could eat it.

Evan couldn't sit still long enough to do more than nibble at his food, and their mom was so upset about the old house she was having trouble eating anything at all.

Laughing to himself as he snuck french fries off their plates, Carson saw that at least their dad was hungry; he was shoveling steak and potatoes into his mouth.

Tale of the Enchanted House

That evening as Robyn was saying goodnight to her children, Marlee asked for a story from the old country, one of the ones great aunt Maggie used to tell their mom. In response, Carson plugged his music back into his ears and turned toward the wall.

Evan asked for either the story about the wing snatchers or the whimsy tree revolt.

"No—they're too spooky!" pleaded Marlee.

"Oh you're just an old scaredy-cat!" said Evan.

As Marlee reached to punch Evan, their mother said, "seeing as we're trying to find a new home and all, what about the Tale of the Enchanted House? I haven't told you that one in ages, and it won't give Marlee any of her nightmares."

Though Carson hated to admit it, he loved this story, too. It just seemed a little childish, seeing as he was going to be fourteen before long. Still, this tale was the beginning of all the old tales from their great-aunt Maggie, a mysterious old lady who had disappeared before Carson got the chance to meet her. It wasn't like she was dead or anything, but maybe she was. His folks said they'd lost touch with her.

As their mother started telling the tale, Carson turned down his music and rolled over to face her.

A long time ago in the old country, there once was an enchanted house named Waterglenn. This house was exceptional in many ways, but mostly in that it was awake. It could think and reason just like we do, and it could communicate with us, too.

Some say this house could do all this because of the particular glen from which its wood came. You see, this area contained a rather large copse of trees on the south side of the glen at the base of a mountain known as Pointers' Peak. Here the trees were quite old, and towered over the landscape beneath them.

Nearby was a waterfall, and it was said that behind the fall lived a community of *trine sprites*.

You know—the type that skimmed over the top of the water much like dragonflies do today, only the trine sprites looked like little people. They averaged a few feet tall or so with double sets of intricately textured wings in all the iridescent colors of the rainbow—emerald green, bright turquoise, radiant orange, shimmering silver, and more.

When the trine sprites swam underwater, which they liked to do on a warm summer's day, they glowed from above as they raced around their pool.

Well, the trine sprites prided themselves on taking care of their surroundings, especially the whimsy trees that grew tall and strong around them. Each year on the Summer Solstice, they would celebrate the summer by feeding their new young whimsy trees the enchanted water from their pond.

It was said that the trees cared for by the trine sprites were born awakened, and stayed awake even when cut down, as long as they had first granted their permission. This granting of permission took place during the Winter Solstice, when the whimsies were sleepy and tired from all the growing they had done during the prior summer.

There was also a ceremony attached to this permission-granting, and the trine sprites supervised this ceremony to ensure that the whimsies being cut were ready to change shape and become a home for people to live in. Chopping down too young or immature a whimsy could have a disastrous effect not only on those who built something with its wood, but on the tree itself; it could die, become confused, or worse—it could create a crazy house.

The family that built and lived inside Waterglenn's walls had a mother, Maggie, a father, Robert, and three children consisting of an older boy—Laird—and fraternal twins, Emilie and Jack. Plus the mother's niece, Fiona. She also had a cat and a dog that tended to scratch her walls and floors, so she was kept busy polishing them most of the day, particularly in the winter months.

Nodding his head, Carson almost fell asleep—until something started nagging at him. Since coming to Waters End, he'd felt different, and his mother's story was reminding him of a life he seemed to remember from another time and place. He didn't understand this other life. After all, he had always been Carson Owen MacKenzie, firstborn in his family, yet his mother's tale was reminding him of another life he may have led.

In his dream, he could see the house named Waterglenn, and he could see his twin siblings, but they didn't look the same. He saw the family of five, so similar to his own, but what spooked him the most was that his mysterious great-aunt Maggie was not just the mother to these children—she was his mother, and he knew what she looked like: flaming-red hair and blue-green eyes just like his own.

How could I know this? he asked himself.

Then, completely alert once more, he listened intently to the remainder of the tale.

As the children started growing up they developed special interests, and Waterglenn accommodated those interests. Laird loved music and played many instruments, wrote, and sang songs. Waterglenn approved of this and created a room within a room for Laird to keep all his instruments, including his baby grand piano.

Emilie loved reading and writing stories and poetry, and Waterglenn approved of this as well by creating a special library to hold the thousands of books Emilie read and saved.

Jack, on the other hand, loved sports and fighting mythical battles. Though Waterglenn did not mind the sports, as they were mainly carried out outside her walls, she did not care for the battles, so she built Jack a room within which he could store his swords, suits of armor, and other battle gear, and then she made him a special wafting window through which he could go fight his battles, and by which she could still watch him and keep him safe.

It was rumored that Fiona, Maggie's niece, was part trine sprite herself, for she was petite, and seemed to manage Waterglenn's grounds without ever lifting a spade or a shovel. At least, no one ever actually saw her doing the work, but they always saw the results in the abundance of fruits, vegetables, herbs, and flowers from Waterglenn's gardens.

One day, this family left Waterglenn and did not return. Some say they drowned out on the loch when their ship capsized in rough weather. Others say they were set upon by highwaymen. To this day, Waterglenn is still missing her family, and waits patiently for their return. She has allowed no one to enter her doors or windows, and protects herself from weather and age with the power handed down to her from Princess Toral, her guardian trine sprite.

As their mother finished the story, she looked over to see all three children sound asleep. Gently she eased Marlee from her lap and into her own bed. She lifted the covers all the way to Marlee's chin the way Marlee liked them. Turning out the lights, she left the door open between their two rooms. For some reason she had yet to discover, Marlee was prone to nightmares, and change—like moving to a new town—seemed to increase their occurrence.

But Carson was not actually asleep. As soon as their mother left the room, he sat up, no longer comfortable in his bed. Though the lights were out, he could see his brother and sister clearly with the help of the nightlight in their bedroom.

"This is so friggin' weird. I am not Laird of Waterglenn," he said aloud. "But I know him, I feel my hands on the piano, and I don't play it."

Obviously not completely asleep, Evan rolled over from his bed. "You playing piano?

Hah! That's the day I'll start singing the blues, bro. Go to sleep, you're creeping me out."

Punching his brother lightly on the shoulder, Carson laughed with him before eventually falling into a fitful sleep.

Nothing Fits

The next day was bright, sunny, and warm. Carson did not care for the heat, so this climate change was a bit difficult for him. His whole family had fair skin and turned bright red in minutes without suntan lotion number thirty or higher. He and Evan were already a mass of freckles from their first experiences in the sun. They took after their dad in that way. His mom and Marlee just turned red, but didn't get many freckles.

At breakfast, his mom said cheerily, "Well at least we all liked our food this morning and were actually served what we asked for. Who's going to find our new home first?"

"Me, me, me!" shouted Marlee. "I want a house like the one in the story last night."

"Yeah," Evan said, "and I want the house to create a hidden sword room just for me that no one but I can find."

"No such house existed then or now. It was just an old-country faery tale," announced Carson, still unsettled from his dream of the night before.

But Marlee and Evan were not convinced. They felt sure that if they looked hard enough, they'd be able to find such a house.

MAY'S BEST

"Ha!" thought Carson as he reviewed their dad's house-hunting list for the day. There were four houses on it, and he could already tell that none were right for them.

Δ Δ Δ

After visiting and dismissing three of the houses, Carson smiled, checking them off their father's list.

Tired and hungry, they stopped for lunch at May's Best, a small café on the main street of Waters End.

When their waitress came up to their table, she cheerfully asked, "Are you new in town? I'm curious, as I haven't seen you before. And quite frankly, I know everyone here."

Robyn responded first. "My husband's just been transferred to the Bingham Company, and we're staying over at the Green Hotel until we find a home here. In fact, we've been house-hunting all morning and are famished. What do you recommend?"

Ignoring her question for the moment, the waitress said, "My name's Maybell, but everyone around here just calls me May. I was born and raised here. You'll meet a lot of old-timers like myself as you get to know the town, and there's a few new folks like yourselves as well now, what with all that construction going on at the Bingham Company."

"Pleased to meet you, May. I'm Robyn, and my clan here consists of Carson, Evan, and Marlee." Then she cautiously asked about the old house on the windy, tree-lined street named Dolphin Court—the old one with the big front porch and the broken windows.

May was clearly surprised they were interested in that particular house. "Oh my, that house has been empty for years. Some people are even saying it's haunted, but I don't think so." Wistfully, she added, "I remember when the MacKenzie family lived there years ago."

"The MacKenzie family!" Evan burst out. "That's our last name too. How did they spell it? Did they use an 'a' in the Mac, or just the letters Mc?"

"Let me see now," said May as she thought back. "I do believe they used an 'a,' because they originally came from the old country."

"We're from the old country, too," said Marlee quickly. "Well, we didn't come from there, but our ancestors did. You see, Dad's mom was a MacQuen who married a MacKenzie..."

"Stop, Marlee!" cried their mother in exasperation. "May doesn't want to hear our whole family history."

May smiled kindly, then said with a twinkle in her eye, "Well, isn't that a coincidence that you've got the same last name, spelled the same way, and are also from the old country."

Robyn didn't say anything more about the old house, but couldn't help thinking that something really was drawing her to it now. "May," she said, "let's get something to eat. Then, if you have a minute, could you tell us more about that old house and the MacKenzie family that lived there?"

"Sure!" May replied. "Well, today's special is homemade meatloaf with mashed potatoes and gravy. My special dessert is a pear torte drizzled with a sweet, dark chocolate sauce, but it isn't as good as Maggie's. No one made a flakier and crispier pear torte than Maggie."

Remembering his dream of the night before, Carson asked, "Who's Maggie?"

"Oh, Maggie lived at that house you're interested in. She was the best cook and best friend to everyone in town. But let me get your orders in, then we'll talk."

While waiting for the MacKenzies to place their orders, May studied them secretly from beneath her bushy gray brows, and as she did she wondered how odd it was that this new MacKenzie clan had come to Waters End. It wasn't just their last name, but that they were another MacKenzie family of five with an older boy and a set of fraternal twins. Such a coincidence must mean something, as the missing MacKenzie clan also had an older boy and twins.

Thinking back, she remembered a prophecy she'd heard a long time ago—something about a new family mending the damage caused the night of the whimsy tree revolt in the old country. As she recalled the story more clearly, her eyes widened in disbelief, then dimmed. Smiling again, she dismissed the story from her mind.

When May returned with their food, she said, "It's starting to get busy now, so I really don't have much time to talk. If you come back later this afternoon, we could talk more about the old MacKenzie house then."

"Thank you," Robyn replied. "Our afternoon schedule is kind of full, but we'll try."

After they finished eating and Robyn paid the check, Marlee asked, "Can we visit the old house now?"

"Not yet, little one. We have one other house on your father's list to visit first, but it's on the same street, so we'll see the old house soon."

The Mean House

Returning to Dolphin Court, they stopped at a house with a For Sale sign out front. "Mom, I don't like this house," Carson said. "Let's go see the old one you like instead."

"How do you know you don't like it, Carson?" she asked. "We haven't even been inside."

Carson carefully looked the house up and down. "It's kind of a Halloween-ish house, Mom. Look how overgrown it is—and you can't see much of it, only the top of the first floor. And check out those second-story windows. They're tall and narrow; makes me think someone is inside them, hiding and looking out at me from behind those even creepier curtains."

At that moment, a real estate agent walked up to their car and introduced himself. "Hi! I'm Mike Warner. Are you interested in seeing this house?"

Robyn said, "Yes, that's why we're here. But before we do, can you give us some specifics about it?" She quickly listed the items on her husband's list, and then finally asked how long the home had been for sale.

The realtor said, "All those things and more have been replaced in the last few years, and the house has been on the market for two days now."

Robyn was clearly disappointed. "Okay, let's go in and see it. Carson, Evan, Marlee, let's go. Now, please!" she emphasized, as it was obvious they didn't want to do so. All three of them got out of the car in a tumble, but held back walking up the path to the house.

"Does someone still live in this house?" asked Marlee.

"Why yes," said Mr. Warner. "but only one person lives here now, and the house is way too big for one person, which is why he's selling it."

Then Carson asked, "Why does only one person live in this house?"

"Hush now," said their mother. "It isn't polite to ask so many questions."

Mr. Warner laughed, though a bit anxiously. "That's all right. You'll probably hear the story from the locals soon enough. You see, there was a family here, but the wife took ill, and her husband couldn't manage their four children on his own without his wife's help, so his wife's sister came and took them all away a few months ago. Now Mr. Edwards is the only one living here, and he lost his job at the Bingham Company recently when the company reorganized and brought someone new in from out of town to run his old division."

All four of the MacKenzies were stunned by this information.

Concerned, the realtor asked, "Did I say something wrong? Mr. Edwards is not at home, if that's what's bothering you."

"Oh no," Robyn said. "But I need a minute alone with the children first, if that's okay with you."

"Sure, sure, take your time," he said, walking toward the front steps, wondering why they were hesitating.

"Kids. I think this house is for sale because your father has been promoted to Mr. Edwards' old job. Now this is the number one house on your father's list, but I'm not comfortable buying the house of a person who just lost his job to your father."

"Me neither," said Carson, breathing a sigh of relief.

"Okay then, we should at least go through the house to please your father, but we need to find reasons your father will understand as to why it won't suit us as a family. Understood?"

They all agreed and proceeded up the walkway to the house with the realtor.

Carson's mom took out her house-hunting notebook and began to note the things none of them liked from the outside. He knew that landscaping alone wouldn't stop their dad from selecting this house, so he hoped they'd find real problems inside.

Mr. Warner gathered them all in the front hall and began pointing out the benefits of the house. It had a large entry hall with wide steps leading up to the second story. On the right, a small sitting room with a brick fireplace could be used as an office. To the left, a large formal living room was anchored by a wide marble fireplace at the end.

As they made their way through the house and the kitchen, Carson noted that some of the boards on the back kitchen porch had recently been replaced. The paint on them had not yet begun to fade, and there was a sickly smell that he couldn't quite identify, so he whispered this to his mom.

In response, Robyn asked the realtor, "Do you smell anything odd?"

When the realtor said no, Robyn said "I do, but I can't put my finger on it. Evan and Marlee, do you smell anything?"

Evan wiggled his nose. "Ick, wick, something trick!"

Marlee pushed him with her elbow. "Yes, Mama. Something does smell bad here, like it died or something." She crinkled her nose to show her displeasure.

Carson looked around again and bluntly pronounced, "There was a cat at school once that had died in an air vent above my homeroom over spring break. It smelled a lot like this."

Curious, Robyn turned to the realtor. "Did Mr. Edwards have a cat?"

The realtor replied, "Not that I know of, but it's possible."

Robyn looked down at the newly replaced floorboards on the back porch and wondered if something had been buried beneath them.

When she looked up, Carson, Evan, and Marlee were already exploring the backyard. She could see that everything was overgrown here as well, and that the lawn hadn't been cut in ages.

"Carson, Evan, Marlee," she called. "Come back inside so we can see the rest of this house. The yard is way too overgrown, and you'll track dirt into the house if you go any farther."

Carson and Evan saw that the yard seemed to go on forever, and it was hard to find the end with all the overgrown shrubs and trees blocking their way. They reluctantly turned around and came back to the house.

As Evan touched the stairway railing, something poked the middle of his hand. "Ow!" he cried out. "This house just bit me!"

"Whatever do you mean, dear?" his mother asked.

His voice rising, Evan said, "Look, Mom. There isn't a splinter in my hand or on the railing, but I have a red spot in the middle of my palm that stings. So it must have bit me!"

Carson and Marlee looked at Evan's hand and agreed that it sure seemed like the house had bitten Evan.

In response, their mom appeared embarrassed, and the real estate agent looked away, trying to pretend he hadn't just witnessed this.

Carson dashed back into the kitchen, took an oven mitt from the stovetop, then ran it over the rail again. Nothing pricked the mitten nor tore at it, so all three children decided that yes, the railing had bitten Evan intentionally. As their mom was already walking away, they just looked at each other seriously, knowing they needed to discuss this later, then turned and followed her.

Once back in the main hallway, the realtor escorted them upstairs. He explained that there were four bedrooms on this floor—the master bedroom with its own bath, and another front bedroom that had its own smaller bathroom. The two rear bedrooms faced the backyard and were connected by a bathroom in between.

Carson noted a huge tree with thick, gnarled branches that almost touched the window of one of the back bedrooms. Though he didn't want this house, he figured that this would be the perfect room for him. He could get in and out of it by climbing up and down that tree.

Evan looked out the window of the bedroom that he might have and studied the backyard. Now he could see where it ended. There was an old stone wall way at the back behind all the shrubs and trees. Before the wall was a dirt mound of some kind—almost hidden, but not quite. He wondered what it was and pulled Carson over to see it.

Just then a shadow passed over the mound, and both brothers thought they saw a small, strange-looking character with pale, lavender skin and a pointy head.

When Marlee walked up and asked them what they were looking at, the brothers slyly looked each other in the eye, blinked once knowingly, then Carson said, "the backyard, silly. We found out where it ends, and that's all we wanted to know."

As Marlee looked up and out the window, Carson mouthed the word 'later' to Evan. Marlee turned around just in time to see this, and knew they weren't telling her something. She frowned and was about to say something when their mother called to them that it was time to leave.

Robyn thanked the realtor for showing them the house, then asked, "Do you know anything about the old house down the block—the one with the big front porch and the broken windows?"

"Hmmm..." Mr. Warner puzzled. "That house has been empty for many years, though I do believe it is still owned by the MacKenzie family estate."

Then Carson asked, "What happened to the family that lived there?"

Shrugging, the realtor said, "I've only been in town a few years myself since the construction boom started, so I really can't say. But isn't your last name MacKenzie as well?" he asked, turning to their mother.

Robyn ignored his question, asking instead if it would be okay to walk around the old house.

"Just be careful if you do," he responded. "Pete's Landscaping Service comes by every month to keep the grounds presentable, but outside of that, the house itself looks like it's falling apart."

Δ Δ Δ

As the family drove away, the mean house was talking to himself.

"Humph! Harrumph! Balderdash and dribble! Humans can be so unkind, even evil. Most of the people who have lived inside my walls were such, and some were even monsters.

I'm glad Edward Edwards is being forced to leave me. Maybe, just maybe I will end up alone like Waterford, then there will be no one trying to control me ever again.

And now another blasted MacKenzie family has walked through my halls and I have had the pleasure of biting one of them. If they dare to live here, I'll make them pay. They won't stay long. I'll see to that for it was a MacKenzie who killed me in the first place!"

The Old House with the Broken Windows

Robyn parked in front of the old house and looked up at it again. Once more she felt something about this house. She felt that it was somehow calling to her, inviting her inside. She shook her head to clear it, then said, "Okay, let's walk around. But remember to be careful, and let's all stay together. Agreed?"

"Yes, Mom," murmured Carson, Evan, and Marlee as they got out of the car.

They looked up at the old house from the sidewalk. They could tell that Pete's Landscaping Service hadn't been here in a while, as weeds were growing up to their shins, and the hedges were getting rather bushy and overgrown.

As they walked up to the front porch, a whisper of a sigh seemed to come from the old house.

Alarmed, Robyn asked, "Did any of you hear something?"

"It was just the wind," Carson replied too quickly as Marlee and Evan shook their heads for 'no' and looked up wide-eyed at the old house.

"Ah-h-h..." came the long drawn out sigh of a sad voice.

This time Robyn knew she had heard something and jumped back a few steps. "Carson, Evan, Marlee, to me—NOW!"

Carson and Evan obeyed her instantly, but Marlee began walking up the steps as if in a trance. She lovingly placed her hand on the railing and patted it as if comforting a hurt friend.

Robyn grabbed Marlee by the back of her red shorts and literally pulled her up and off her feet.

"Ouch!" yelled Marlee as the trance broke and she came back to herself. "Why'd you do that, Mom?"

"This house is haunted silly," Carson said. "Didn't you hear the noises it made as we approached it?"

"It was calling me, inviting me in," Marlee explained. "This house is lonely. I can tell."

Thinking about the faery tale of the house named Waterglenn, Evan decided that this must be a similar house. "Mom, I think it's safe. Let's try this again." And he proceeded to walk up the front steps like Marlee had, but this time the old house made no sound at all.

Evan tested each board as he walked up the steps, then ran his hand lightly over the railing, almost patting it like Marlee had done. He turned around at the top, rather proud of himself. "The steps are solid. They didn't wiggle or anything, and the railing didn't bite me like that mean house did."

Robyn, Carson, and Marlee looked at Evan in amazement. Now all of them were feeling rather foolish, and even though they'd agreed not to walk on the porch, they couldn't help themselves and proceeded up the front steps.

Evan started walking along the front porch, exclaiming how big it was. It must have been a full ten feet deep before the front door and at least thirty feet long. All of it felt solid, so he pretended to skate down to the left end, then let out a whoop as, out of nowhere, a ramp appeared leading down toward the backyard. *Excellent,* he thought, *this is perfect for skateboarding!* Then he thought, *That's odd. This ramp wasn't here a minute ago.*

"Carson, come here!" he called to his older brother. "Isn't this a cool ramp? It's perfect for skateboarding down and up."

Carson looked at Evan. "What ramp?"

Evan turned around and the ramp was gone. The front railing ended right at the end of the house. "What the bleep?" he exclaimed. "I swear a second ago there was a ramp here, and I was about to skate down it."

Marlee and their mother came up at that moment and asked what was going on. Carson said, "Evan's being weird again, Mom. He's delusional—thinks he saw a ramp at the end of the porch. As you can see, there's no ramp."

"But Carson," his mother said, "there *is* a ramp—right behind you."

Now it was Carson's turn to be confused. "I don't get it! I tell you, it wasn't there a minute ago."

Then Evan exclaimed, "It's gone again!"

They all looked for the ramp, and sure enough it no longer existed.

Confused, their mother said, "I could have sworn we just saw a ramp here."

"Aha!" Carson exclaimed. "See, I was right! There's no ramp."

Then Marlee wailed, "But there was a ramp, and we all saw it!"

"Ah-h-h..." came a sad voice once more.

All four of them huddled together, wondering what to do next, when their mother whispered, "This house isn't haunted. It's alive! I think it knows we're here. Evan, what were you doing when that ramp appeared?"

"I was pretending to skate down the porch, and as I came to the end I wanted a ramp to be there so I could skate down and keep on going. There wasn't a ramp at first, but then there was almost as soon as I thought it. It just appeared out of nowhere!"

"Hmmm," murmured their mother, keeping her voice low. "I'm not sure what's going on, but I think we may have stumbled onto a living house like the one I told you about last night. Until now, I thought it was just a faery tale passed down from great-aunt Maggie, but now...I don't know what to think."

"Maggie…" sighed the house. Then a voice entered each of their minds, saying, "Maggie used to live here. She baked the most wonderful desserts."

Startled but not afraid, Robyn asked aloud, "Who are you? And how do you know our Maggie? And more importantly, what are you?"

At that moment, Mr. Warner the realtor walked up and asked with concern, "I'm Mike Warner. Have you forgotten me already? I'm just checking on you, as you said you were coming to look at this old house. Are you okay? You look like you've seen a ghost."

Robyn jumped. Recovering herself quickly, she shook her head and began to apologize. "Sorry, Mike. We were exploring this huge front porch and thought we heard a voice is all. It was probably just a breeze, right kids?"

Carson looked down and said nothing. Evan and Marlee shook their heads up and down in perfect agreement with their mother—until Evan, once again, shook his head left to right.

The realtor said, "Well, it seems that the front porch is solid enough, but you never know with these old houses. I still think you would be safer to just walk the grounds and stay off the porches."

"I think you may be right. Kids, come along. Let's walk around to the side and back of this old house and stay off the porches for now."

"Would you like me to walk with you?" Mr. Warner asked. "I haven't visited this house before and am also curious."

Cautiously, she said, "Yes, maybe that would be a good idea." Though secretly she wished he had not shown up at all.

Δ Δ Δ

Unbeknownst to the family, the old house was indeed alive and examining them carefully. Plus, the three children seemed somehow familiar to him.

Looking at them more closely, the house saw that the older boy had Maggie's light eyes and sunlit hair, and he could see Maggie's husband Robert's chin and nose on the younger boy. But Mr. Warner didn't feel like this family's father; there was no real warmth between him and them.

Wait and watch, said the old house to himself. He would study them just as they appeared to be studying him.

Δ Δ Δ

The MacKenzies and the realtor left the front porch and proceeded around the right side of the house toward the back. There was a wide and high stone wall overgrown with vines, but with a slightly rusted, unlocked iron gate that the realtor opened easily for them. They walked through one at a time, with Carson in the lead and Mr. Warner at the rear, leaving the old gate open before he too stepped into the backyard.

In the center of the backyard, and set well away from the house, was a most unusual tree. It was much taller than the house and had wide and thick, well-spaced branches. In some respects it looked like a pine tree, except that the long needles seemed to have some kind of soft and fuzzy fur growing on them that appeared to change color as its branches swayed in the afternoon breeze.

"This is great!" Carson said. "This house has a climbing tree. Come on Evan, let's go!"

Carson and Evan raced to the tree and began climbing up through the branches quick as monkeys to see who could get the highest.

At just under five feet tall, Marlee couldn't reach the first branch above her. She cried aloud that it wasn't fair her brothers got to climb the tree and she could not.

Her mother looked over. "But Marlee, you can reach the first branch. Just put your hand out."

Marlee turned once more and saw to her amazement that yes, she could reach the first branch, though she knew she couldn't have a minute ago. In haste she began to climb, trying to catch up to her brothers.

The realtor asked Mrs. MacKenzie if she always allowed her children to climb trees, and wasn't she worried about them falling?

"Why no, Mike!" she laughed. "I swear they could climb trees before they could walk. You should have seen them in our old home in Oak Grove. Why, look at them now! If I didn't know better, I'd say they were flying up that tree instead of climbing it, and that is a most unusual tree. Do you have any idea what kind it is?"

The realtor, skeptical about children climbing trees in the first place, mumbled,

"No, I haven't seen a tree like this before myself."

While Robyn watched her children, she did not notice that the tree was actually lowering its branches slightly as each child approached, then lifting them up to the next branch. All she heard were peals of laughter from all three of them as they neared the top of the tree.

Thrilled, Carson yelled down, "I can see the whole town from up here."

"Me too," shouted Evan.

As the smallest and lightest, Marlee could climb even higher than her brothers. She squealed, "I can see the whole town too, Mom. And the water beyond. This is the best tree in the whole wide world!"

Robyn shaded her eyes against the midday sun and tried to see the three of them. What she saw instead were shaking boughs and limbs with a peek of Evan's turquoise t-shirt and Marlee's red shorts shining through the branches. Carson was in a dark-green t-shirt and black jeans, so she couldn't locate him at all.

Δ Δ Δ

The old house was trying to be quiet, but he so loved having children play in his tree again. He made sure to ask the tree to dull her needle points to avoid pricking the children's arms and legs as they climbed. Also, he laughed aloud by making creaking and popping sounds, and this time no one was the wiser, as they thought these the sounds of the branches and twigs.

He decided then and there that this was a family he would like to come live with him. But how to invite them when they got so nervous when he tried to talk to them? And again the old house wondered about the connection between his Maggie and this family.

Δ Δ Δ

Robyn decided that she wanted this house, even though it was strange, and even though she hadn't been inside it yet. But how to convince her husband when the other house was for sale and this one was not?

Turning to Mr. Warner, she asked him how she could find out if the house was for sale or lease. He informed her she could check with the local solicitor.

Placing her hands firmly around her mouth to focus the direction and intensity of her voice, she looked up at the tree again. "Carson, Evan, Marlee...come down. NOW!"

Slowly arms and legs reappeared, and finally the bodies of her three children as they neared the ground once more. In surprise she saw not a scratch, not a tear in their clothes, and not a single needle in their hair. *How could this be?*

As they walked back to the gate, they found it shut, but the realtor remembered clearly that he had left it open. Thinking a breeze may have blown it closed, he tried the latch and it would not give. Frustrated, he said, "It won't take but a minute. I think this latch is old and sticks, is all."

Carson did not like the realtor, so he walked up and with a quick flick of his fingers lifted the latch and opened the gate.

In her concern over what Mr. Warner might think, Robyn said, "You know, Carson plays sports. He's strong for his age. Don't give it another thought."

But the realtor did give it another thought, as he was no slouch himself, and the gate wouldn't open for him.

"Don't go..." came a low, creaky voice from above their heads.

The realtor looked uncomfortable, causing Carson to say rather smugly, "Oh, that's just the wind. Are you scared?"

"Why, no. Nothing of the kind. Aren't you coming as well?" the realtor inquired as he quickly exited through the gate.

Robyn tried to say goodbye to him, but he swiftly walked down the block toward the other house that she knew her husband would want instead of this one.

As soon as he left, the old house tried speaking to them again. He simply said, "Stay."

All the MacKenzies were rather stunned to hear the house speak to them once more. So Carson asked, "How can you talk to us?"

Then silently and into their minds via telepathy, the old house replied, "I don't know. I just know that I can when I want to."

Then Evan asked, "Did you make that skateboard ramp off the front porch when we first walked up your steps?"

Worried about what they would think, the house reluctantly answered, "Yes, I did."

Confused, Evan asked, "Then why did you take it away again?"

Miserable now, as he truly didn't know what would please them, the old house said, "Because I thought you wanted it, then I thought your brother didn't. Then I didn't know what you wanted."

"Cool," Evan and Carson said together.

Marlee wondered what happened to the old house's family and why was he all alone now. The house told her that they disappeared a long time ago and he has missed them all this time, and waited for them to come back.

Robyn turned to her daughter and saw an intense look in her eyes. Disturbed, she asked, "Marlee! What's going on here?"

With eyes full of innocence, Marlee said, "I'm just talking with the house."

Concerned, Robyn said, "But I didn't hear anything."

"That's because we were having a private conversation, Mom."

Frustrated, Robyn asked, "A private conversation about what?"

"About why this house is so lonely," said Marlee, a bit contritely.

"Well, why is this house so lonely, then?" asked her mother.

"Because it lost its family and is now the only house on the block without one," Marlee replied, pleased to be able to tell her mother something she didn't already know for once.

"But there is another house that almost has no family down the street," Carson said. "You know, Mr. Edwards' house."

The old house suddenly shuddered and moaned for all of them to hear, "Not that house. It's dead. It can't talk anymore."

"It can't be dead," Evan said. "It bit me earlier today when we walked through it."

"What do you mean, it bit you?" asked the old house.

So Evan proceeded to tell the house about the puncture wound on his hand, and showed his palm to the front of the old house.

"So!" replied the old house. "That house isn't dead, then. I wonder if it just turned mean because of the families who have lived in it?"

"There's just one person living in it now," Carson said. "It's the man who lost his job to our father at the Bingham Company. Mom knows that Dad will want to buy that house, and we can't because we don't like it. We wanna live here, not there."

Getting excited, the old house asked, "You want to live here, with me?"

"Yes," they all said as one.

"But you aren't for sale, as far as we can tell," said Robyn sadly. "At least, there's no For Sale sign out front."

"Well, can't you just move in?" asked the old house in confusion.

"No, things aren't done that way," Robyn replied. "We either need to purchase or lease you from the owner or a business that represents the owner."

"But I don't know where my missing family is," wailed the old house. "If I did, I could ask them for you."

Thinking of the possibilities, Robyn said, "House, let us see what we can find out. We'll come back soon, we promise."

Marlee turned to face them all. "His name is Waterford."

"Why, how do you know that?" asked her mother, followed shortly by an exasperated,

"Oh, never mind. House, is your name Waterford?"

"Yes, and you can call me Ford for short. That's what my missing family called me."

"Amazing!" was all Robyn could say as she started for the car.

"We'll be back!" Carson said, mimicking the hero from a movie he liked.

Robyn was truly flabbergasted. She couldn't wrap her mind around the fact that Waterford was a living house like in her great-aunt Maggie's faery tales. "Kids," she said at last, "don't say anything to your father about this house talking to us. Not yet. I don't think he'll believe us."

"That's for sure," Carson said. "I wouldn't have believed it either. Not in a gazillion years!"

Father Knows Best

At dinner that night, their father asked how their house-hunting went. Robyn, Carson, Evan, and Marlee just looked at each other for a moment meaningfully before their mother produced her notebook describing the pros and cons of the houses they'd visited.

All four of them knew the instant he came to the note on 'this house belongs to Edward Edwards,' as their father had already told them several stories about the man who had his new job before him... It seemed Mr. Edwards managed by intimidation instead of cooperation, making for a poorly-run division that hadn't grown successfully.

Nelson did not pause for long, or even look up at his family as he continued nodding his head, saying things like, "We can replace the landscaping; that's no issue. Hmmm, no family room, that's not good. But five bedrooms and four recently remodeled bathrooms...excellent for this price. And this house is about fifteen minutes from my work. Nice indeed!"

He beamed at his family. "Thank you all. I do believe you have found the perfect house for us. I'll call the realtor and ask for my own viewing."

"But dear, how can you buy the house of the man whose job you just took?" pleaded Robyn. "You must see now why that house won't suit us."

"This has nothing to do with Mr. Edwards." Nelson replied,. " We don't have the time or the money to enjoy the luxury of emotionalism when choosing a purchase as big as a house! Besides, you can redecorate it within reason and make it warm and inviting like you have all our previous homes."

Unable to stay quiet any longer, Evan yelled, "But Dad, that house bit me today!"

"What!" their father asked.

"It did—right here." Evan showed his father the puncture wound on the palm of his left hand.

"Ridiculous!" said their father, trying not to laugh out loud.

Carson immediately came to Evan's defense. "It's true, Dad. We looked and there were no splinters on the handrail anywhere, but when Evan touched it, it bit him. Honest!"

"Why, Carson! As the oldest, I expect you to have a more reasonable head on your shoulders. How could you even suggest such an outlandish notion? Humph!"

Chuckling a bit, Nelson turned to his daughter. "Now Marlee, tell your father what really happened to Evan."

"It's true, Dad. And that's not the worst of it. Mr. Edwards killed his cat and buried it under the back porch and it stinks!" Marlee replied, her voice rising in support of her twin.

"Not you too, Marlee. Moving to Waters End seems to have made my whole family a bit batty. I think we should turn in early tonight; it's obvious today was too much for all of you. Trust me, you'll feel better in the morning. And once we move into our new home, everyone will get on a regular schedule and all these fantasies will disappear."

"But Nelson dear, all four of us dislike that house immensely. Don't our votes count for anything?" Robyn pleaded.

Ending the conversation once and for all, Nelson said, "Robyn. Houses cost a considerable amount of money—not just to purchase, but to maintain. Therefore, we must make a business-minded decision. For all the other faults Mr. Edwards may have had, I believe his choice in a home was smart, and I like the way he maintained it. He took care of the essentials."

Δ Δ Δ

That evening while saying goodnight to her children, Robyn said, "I'm so sorry. Somehow we'll have to make the best of this, as once your father's mind is made up, there is nothing I can do to change it." Then she kissed them goodnight and left the door slightly ajar as always.

In the other room, Carson listened for the sound of his mother's soft snore. As soon as he was convinced that she had fallen asleep, he slipped from his bed and motioned for Marlee and Evan to join him in the bathroom.

Carson started it off with, "Maybe if we talk to May? She seemed to know more than what we already heard today."

Then Evan said, "But the mean house did bite me. Maybe if we go back there we can find something else wrong with it?"

Marlee didn't want to go back to the mean house. She asked, "But what if that Mr. Edwards is there? I mean, if he killed his cat, what might he do to us?"

"Well," Carson replied, "what if we go back to Ford and ask him more about the mean house? Maybe he can help us come up with something to convince Dad not to buy it."

Both Evan and Marlee liked that idea, but Marlee saw a little problem with it. "But how do we get there without Mom or Dad knowing about it?"

Carson's eyes lit up. "We could go right now."

"Oh!" Evan replied. "But I'm sleepy now."

Then Marlee said, "It's dark outside and late. Oh wait! I've got an idea. Mom's getting her hair done tomorrow morning. What if we go with her, then ask if we can walk through the park, but really, we'll go visit Ford? We could agree to meet at May's Best for lunch."

Both Evan and Carson liked that idea, and Carson added, "And while we're talking to Ford, let's ask him about Waters End. This is the best town we've lived in so far, and I want to live with Ford, too."

LOOKING FOR ANSWERS

The next morning when their mother popped her head through the adjoining doorway, she was surprised to see Carson, Marlee, and Evan dressed and ready to go down to breakfast even before their father.

"Why the early start?"

Carson explained, "We want to walk around town and explore our new surroundings."

"Great! I'm going into town to get my hair done. Why don't I drop you off on my way in, then we could meet at May's for lunch?"

As this was exactly what Carson, Evan, and Marlee had planned, they quickly agreed.

Δ Δ Δ

As soon as their mother entered the hair salon, they took off for Dolphin Court and the old house. On the way, they talked again about what questions they wanted to ask the old house.

Evan started it this time with, "We need to find out more about the mean house so we can stop Dad from buying it."

"Check!" said his siblings.

Then Carson said, "And we need to learn more about Waterford, how come he can talk to us, and if he was made from the whimsy trees like in Mom's story."

Evan and Marlee agreed, then Marlee said, "And we need to find out about the Maggie connection. We MacKenzies could be related to Ford's missing family."

They were so deep in conversation, fine-tuning their questions as they walked the mile or so to Dolphin Court, that they almost missed it. All of a sudden Marlee shrieked, and Carson and Evan spun around quickly to see a little man with pale, lavender skin, a pointed head and a bright-green cape disappear behind the hedges of the mean house.

"Oh my gosh!" shouted Evan. "That's the weird guy we saw from the bedroom window of the mean house yesterday. He looks like a pointer pair from one of Mom's old stories."

Surprised, Marlee asked, "Is that what you were keeping from me yesterday? Is that really a pointer?"

"Could be," replied Evan. "And the pointers always travel in pairs, so there must be another one close by. Let's see if we can find him."

"Not yet," said Carson. "We have too many questions for Ford and not much time this morning. Race you there!"

All three took off in a run with little Marlee pulling ahead, as she loved the feel of the wind on her face—and besides, she loved beating her brothers in any game, as she so seldom could.

As they neared the old house, Marlee sprinted up the steps two at a time, laughing.

She turned around to gloat at her brothers when she saw another pointer leap over the rail at the end of the long front porch and disappear toward the back of the house. Again she yelled to her brothers, who barely got a glimpse of another bright-green cape disappearing over the railing as they came up behind her.

All of a sudden the words, "Where's the fire, little MacKenzies?" entered their minds in a stern but kindly manner. They realized that, in their excitement at seeing a second pointer in a matter of minutes, they had not said hello to Waterford.

"Who was that person that just leapt over your railing, Ford?" asked Carson.

"Hello, Waterford," said Marlee, followed closely by, "Don't be rude, Carson. Say hello first."

"Sorry," said Carson. "Hello, Ford. But what or who was that?"

"Who was whom?" replied Waterford.

Frustrated, Evan said, "That guy with the pointed head that just jumped over your railing."

"Oh, that!" replied Waterford blandly. "Why he's a pointer, I guess. Don't know which one, as they all look alike to me."

All three of them raced to the end of the porch and leaned out over the railing to see if the pointer was still there.

"Gone," sighed Evan.

"Ya," said Marlee.

"Darn," Carson joined in.

"Why are you so sad?" Waterford asked.

Evan looked at Waterford, wondering how Ford could see him when he didn't appear to have any eyes.

Waterford answered that he could see them through his senses as opposed to the physical eyes that humans have, and because he could see thus, he could see a lot farther than they could.

"Ah-ha!" laughed Evan, followed by, "That's so cool!"

"What's so cool?" asked Marlee.

"Why, how Ford can see, silly. Didn't you hear him answer my question about how he can see when he doesn't have any eyes?"

"No I didn't, because you only thought the question, silly yourself. Ford only answers all of us when we ask him things out loud. Isn't that right, Ford?"

"Yes, Miss Marlee, it is. I am a proper house. I have learned to talk to people selectively based on how they communicate with me." Then Waterford began to sigh again, and the front porch swayed ever so gently, though not enough to knock the MacKenzie children down, as it was more like a gentle rolling motion.

"What's wrong, Ford?" Marlee asked. "Did we do something to make you sad?"

"No children, you did not. Talking with you reminds me of my missing family, and I have been so lonesome for so long."

Knowing that this was one of the questions they wanted answered, Carson asked, "Does it hurt to talk about them?"

"Why, no. In fact, it makes me happy. Do you want to hear about them then?"

"Yes!" all three said at once.

So the old house began telling the children about his missing family.

People used to come here often. There was fun, games, and singing—and the food! Neighbors could smell the delicious aromas floating through the breeze when Maggie baked her Scottish shortbread, lemon cakes, fudge brownies, and a confection she called "teenage cookies," which were made up of oats, butter, vanilla, sugar, and various flavors of jam.

Between people and animals, quite a few have lived with me over the years.

My oldest human family member was Maggie, our wonderful cook. Also, I'm pretty sure it was Maggie's family who made me. They came to Waters End from somewhere in the old country. The other houses and I believe that our being awake has something to do with Maggie and her family.

Maggie had three children who also had children, then more children, but they're all gone now.

We also had a dog named Alice—Ali, for short. She was a Finnish Lapphund and felt it was her job to herd the family back together whenever they'd wander too far apart. She disappeared the same night as my last human family members.

One day everything was fine and normal, then the next they were all gone. It isn't like they left on vacation. They just disappeared one night while I was sleeping. It took a while before I realized my family wasn't coming back. I waited and waited. Then one day, one of my windows cracked, then two or three of them followed in quick succession. When the cool night air started blowing onto my walls and floors, I wondered if anyone would ever come visit me or live with me again.

Oh, I could fix my windows, but I've become so sad I don't feel like it. In fact, I've been so sad that I've begun to moan at the oddest times, usually around dawn or dusk, or whenever the wind blows. Then again, sometimes I'm just so sad that I don't care and I moan anyway, especially if I see that mean boy from down the block—the one that cracked my windows. His name is Edward Edwards. His father thought it amusing to give him two almost-the-same names, but I think it just adds to his nastiness.

Of course, Edward isn't a little boy anymore, but I still know who he is, and he still has that same mean look on his face, and lives in that same house down the block. In fact, I bet it's his meanness that killed that house. We other houses on the block have discussed this for a long, long time, and believe it must be so, as that house no longer talks to any of us, so that family must have done something bad to it.

Thrilled, Evan interrupted him. "So you houses can talk to each other, too? Can we talk to them, then?"

"Yes, I suppose so, but I'd need to introduce you first. You see, not all the houses on Dolphin Court are as close to their families as I am, or was," Ford replied.

"Can all you houses do the same things, like talk to people and take care of yourselves when you want to?" asked Marlee.

"Some houses are more awake than others," Ford replied, then sighed long and slow as he continued. "Most of us houses love our families except, of course, for the mean house. I've often wondered if that house was just sleeping, waiting for Edward Edwards and his family to leave. You see, all we houses know is that one day we did not exist, then the next we did.

"I think I remember being some kind of a tree once, but that was in another lifetime, long before I ever became the house I am today. Besides, the other houses on Dolphin

Court laugh at me when I tell them this, so I keep my thoughts to myself now. I have so much time to think these days because my family isn't here."

"Gosh!" Carson sympathized. "That's awful, Ford. No wonder you are so sad. Do you remember where you were a tree? I mean, before you became a house, that is."

"Hmmm... For some reason I think I lived near water, as I remember falling asleep to the sound of water splashing close by."

"And you have no idea what happened to your family?" asked Evan.

"No, I don't," replied Waterford. "However, I do remember that when I awoke as a house, my first resident was Maggie's brother, the Captain Jon Dinsmore. He taught me what I could and could not do; mainly that the first rule of all us houses is to do no harm."

"Ha!" exclaimed Evan. "Someone should have told that to the mean house."

"He's always been different from the rest of us. He was the second built, as I was the first house on this street and was lonesome sometimes when the captain was away. Then when Maggie and her family came, more houses were built, and we found we could talk to each other as well as our families."

"Ford," asked Marlee out loud, "could your missing Maggie be the same as our missing Maggie? I mean, if that's true, then your missing family might be our relatives, too."

"I don't know," Waterford replied. "I've never been good at measuring time like my human family members can."

Still curious about the Maggie connection, Marlee continued, "Ford, how long did Maggie live with you?"

"Hmmm..." said Waterford. "Maggie's always been here, at least as far back as I can remember."

'Hmmm...-back!' thought Carson. *There's no way Ford's missing Maggie could be that old.*

Just as Carson was about to ask why Waterford couldn't remember, a pointer flashed past them yet again. And this time it was Evan who saw him first.

"Look," he cried, "another pointer!"

"Ford," asked Carson, "is this the same pointer we saw when we arrived?"

"I'm not sure," Ford replied. "Usually I see one of them every year or so, and now three times in the same day. This is quite odd indeed!"

Then Marlee said, "Uh-oh, it's almost lunchtime. We're supposed to meet Mama at noon at May's café. If we don't leave now, she may get worried."

"Not now!" cried Carson. "We need to understand this pointer thing, and the Maggie connection. Now we have even more questions than when we got here today."

Marlee already knew her brothers well enough to let them figure it out themselves. The last thing she wanted to be was another version of her mother to them. *Uh-uh,* she thought to herself. *There is no way they are going to end up blaming me for not getting their questions answered.*

Then she shuddered, because Waterford had heard her thoughts and in a kind, grandfatherly tone he said, "Don't worry, little one. Yes, there is a mystery here, and we will solve it together. I'm used to having many children run around me, and you know how much I miss that. So you must also know that I understand Carson and Evan's curiosity. They express themselves differently than you do. This is all good. Between the four of us, we will learn what happened. I so want you and your family to come live with me."

Marlee looked up at the old house as she walked down the porch steps and whispered, "I understand, too. See you soon, Ford."

And into her mind came his reply, "Tomorrow, then?"

"Yes," said Marlee. "We'll be back tomorrow, somehow."

As the three MacKenzie children walked down Dolphin Court, they looked back frequently and waved to Ford until they could no longer see him.

More Questions

The whole way back to the café, Carson and Evan were trying to spot another Pointer, while Marlee lagged a bit behind them, thinking about Ford's missing family.

May greeted and seated them when they walked into the café, then told them their mother had been held up at the hair salon. She asked if they'd like a soda while they waited for her. Carson and Evan asked for root beer floats, and Marlee wanted lemonade.

When May brought their drinks over, Carson leaned toward her and whispered, "Are there any short people in town with pale skin and kinda pointy heads?"

May looked at him quizzically for a moment. "Carson, why do you ask such a question? Have you seen people like that in Waters End?"

Before Carson could answer, Evan blurted out, "Yes! And this morning we saw three of them, but we couldn't tell if it was the same one three times or three different ones."

Both Carson and Marlee glared at Evan, as they felt May would think they were all crazy. As they turned toward May to see her reaction, she was looking at them with an odd expression.

Slowly she nodded her head for yes, then lowered her voice. "We need to discuss this in private. I need to do a little digging myself to see what's going on. The last time pointers showed up in such numbers was shortly before Maggie and her family went missing."

All three MacKenzie children were silenced by May's statement. Though Marlee's mouth shaped itself into a big 'O,' no sound did she make.

Emboldened by May's last answer, Carson asked, "May, is the old house alive?"

This time May was truly stunned. Looking at Carson seriously, she said, "You wouldn't be asking me if you didn't already know the answer, but what you don't know is the why or the how. Am I correct?"

"Yes, May. We seem to have stumbled upon a few riddles. Mom thinks the house—Ford's his name—is missing his family like in the *Tale of Enchanted House*," Carson said, looking at May, hopeful of learning more.

"That he is, Carson MacKenzie," May replied with a knowing look. "I'll be back in a minute," she said as a new customer entered her café.

When May went off to handle the new customer, it was as if a spell had been broken and all three began madly guessing what this could mean. They were in the middle of this discussion when their mother walked in.

"Walking through town must have been good for you." Robyn smiled as she approached the table. "You seem excited and happy. That makes me happy, too. So! What adventures did you have this morning? I want to hear it all."

Carson evaded her question by quickly saying, "Your hair looks great, Mom!" Which gave Evan and Marlee time to compose themselves as well.

"Ya, Mom," said Evan, "you look like a movie star."

"Can I get my hair done too, Mom?" asked Marlee.

Robyn was pleased by their compliments, but not fooled for one minute. "I wonder what you three have been up to? Your clothes are still clean, so I can see you weren't out conquering the world, but something's not right here. Could it possibly be that only Marlee ever compliments me on my hair?" she ended with a grin.

Marlee came to her brothers' defense. "Mom, I'm trying to train them to be good husbands one day."

Laughing, Robyn decided to let her questions go for the moment. She was famished and thirsty after sitting in the hair salon.

May spotted Robyn's entrance and came over to take their lunch orders.

Robyn apologized for not making it back over yesterday, as they had ended up visiting the old house on Dolphin Court. Then she asked if May had any time today to talk about the house. "It is a most peculiar property," Robyn said. "We really want to know more about its history."

"I'm a bit short-handed this afternoon," May said. "Perhaps you could pop by after tomorrow's breakfast rush, say ten-ish?"

"That works. Oh, and Nelson's already selected a different home for us on Dolphin Court—the one just around the bend from the old house."

Rather surprised, May asked, "You don't mean the Edwards house, do you?"

Nodding her head sadly, Robyn answered, "Why yes, that's the one."

"That wouldn't have been my first choice," said May. "A lot of bad luck with that house over the years—what with the deaths, and now Mr. Edwards losing his job. Not that he was ever a friendly person to begin with."

What's a Pointer Pair?

That evening when she was saying goodnight to her children, Carson asked,

"Mom, can you tell us more about the pointer pairs?"

"But Carson, what about Marlee's nightmares?"

"I don't mind, Mom. Really," Marlee said. "What I don't want to hear about is the wing snatcher creature thingies."

"Well, if you're sure," their mother replied. When all heads bobbed yes, she began to tell them what she knew of the pointer pairs.

The pointer pairs come from the old country; at least, we think they do. No one really knows for sure. They are a most curious race, as they are shorter than we are, have lavender-hued skin, pointed heads, and no body hair whatsoever, even on their heads.

In the old world, the pointer pairs were known as mystics who, when called upon, could assist with the outcomes of various situations. To my knowledge, they always travel in pairs, and each pair appears to be an odd combination. One silly pair that great-aunt Maggie used to tell me about was Dither and Dawn. Dither had a way of creating confusion wherever he went, and Dawn brought clarity to that confusion.

For instance, there was a time when Maggie thought she might have met this pair of pointers, though I'm sure she said that just to amuse me. She said she'd run into Dither quite by accident. She was walking on her way home from somewhere when Dither bumped into her. He was mumbling something to himself, and neither had seen the other. Maggie excused herself and tried to continue on home when Dither started to follow her.

"Why are you following me?" asked Maggie politely.

"Because I forgot where I was going when you bumped into me," replied Dither.

"But I didn't bump into you. You bumped into me," replied Maggie, a little surprised.

"Oh! Then do you know where I was going?" asked Dither hopefully.

"How would I know what your business is?" replied Maggie. "I don't even know your pointer pair name, so we should not be speaking in the first place."

Just then, another pointer appeared. "This way, Dither." And the pair disappeared into the woods on the other side of the road without saying another word to Maggie.

Because Maggie had heard of the pointer pair named Dither and Dawn, she knew the second pointer had to be Dawn. Plus, the old tale said that once you knew a pointer by name, the pointer must come whenever you called him.

Perhaps the most curious thing about these beings is that each pair has another name that represents the two of them in an odd sort of way. If ever you want to call them both, you can only do so by calling their together name.

So, let's see. There are many pairs of pointers, and it is not always easy to tell one pair from the next. Plus, you must know their correct individual names as well as their together name. It is a high insult to call one by the other's name. In fact, you may never get the chance to speak to them again if you botch their naming the first time you try, as they've been known to hold grudges forever.

However, if you did want to call a pointer pair for some reason, you would go to a place called Pointers' Peak. In the old country, this was on a tall mountain high above the home of the trine sprites and the whimsy trees, and there were

Dolphin Court   Page 77

several caves you would need to avoid, because most of the creatures that lived inside them were not friendly. These creatures never seemed to bother the pointers, though. In fact, I don't remember if the pointers fear anything.

Also, they say that when pointers are seen in large numbers, something unexpected is about to happen. Maggie told me that many pointers were seen right before the enchanted house named Waterglenn lost her family.

This time as their mother finished her story, all three of her children were still alert and wide awake. She sighed. "Well, I guess that was too short a story for you to fall asleep on."

"It's okay, Mom," Carson said. "Can you tell us anything else about the pointers?"

"Well, dear," she replied, "I know there are other pairs, and I may remember some of their names from Maggie's tales. But why this sudden interest?"

Coming to the rescue, Marlee said, "Mom, we invented a new game as we were walking through town today. One of us was a pointer, and the others were trying to guess which one.

But we didn't know many pointer names, so we couldn't play the game very well."

"Oh so that's what you were up to today when I walked in on you at the café!" she exclaimed. "Now your excitement makes sense. I should have guessed it was another of your infamous games. It must have been Waterford that got you on this train of thinking. I still can't believe he's a living house. And if he truly is, then I guess pointer pairs could be real as well. Hmmm...speaking of which, let's visit Waterford again tomorrow after we talk to May down at the café. I've got more questions for him, and I bet you do, too. Now I think it really is bedtime for you three."

"But Mom," Carson almost whined, "you were going to tell us about a few more pointers."

"Oh, I forgot. You need some more names for your game, right?"

As her children smiled and nodded back, she continued, "Well, let's see... There are Waste-Not and Want-Not. They are a funny pair in that Waste-Not is a pack rat, kind of like you, Carson," she teased, "and Want-Not is kind of like you, Evan, in that you never seem to need anything—not even food. I swear, you live in your own world sometimes.

"Maggie also said something about Want-Not having the power to make someone feel happy without doing anything. It may sound odd, but remember that new bicycle you wanted so badly two years ago, Carson?"

When Carson nodded, she went on to say, "If you had visited Want-Not, you wouldn't have felt the need to have that bicycle any longer."

Carson thought a moment, then nodded. "So what would happen if no one wanted anything new any longer, mom?"

"I'm not sure, dear. The economy would most likely suffer, as people wouldn't be buying so many things they really don't need. In fact, people would probably find out that many of the things they think they need, they don't, just like you didn't need that new bicycle, as you already had an old one that worked just fine. It wasn't shiny and new. It wasn't blue. It didn't have those big tires that you wanted, but it worked. Now off to bed with you."

As their mother left the room, the three of them quietly began discussing what to do next. Evan began by thanking Marlee for her quick thinking about the pointer pair game.

Later, as they were dropping off to sleep, Carson reminded them both, "We need to be more careful around mom, you know. She gets nervous too quickly and might interfere with us getting our questions answered."

May's Midnight Visit

True to her word, May couldn't wait to close her café that evening and find out what was going on with the return appearance of so many pointer pairs to Waters End. She began by driving over to Dolphin Court and stopping about a block away from Waterford. She looked carefully to make sure no one was about, then walked quickly and quietly up to the house.

From there, she again looked around slowly to ensure no one else was present, especially a pointer, as they could be so sly. When she was satisfied there were no pointers—or people for that matter—instead of going up the front walk, she went through the side gate and into the backyard. Once more she looked for signs of any other visitors, then breathed a sigh of relief.

Though she needed to talk to Waterford, she decided to check her vegetable garden and other plantings first. There were no lights at all in the garden, but May didn't need them.

She was glad for the cover of darkness with a slim and dim moon above.

As she worked, her thoughts returned to Maggie. *What could have happened to her, and why has she not contacted me all these years?* "I would know if she was dead," she said to herself. "I've still enough trine sprite blood in me to know these things. I may be old, but not near as old as Maggie."

Too many pieces of the puzzle, she concluded. And now this new MacKenzie family had come to town. Again she thought of the prophecy of old, and just as quickly dismissed it from her mind. *I will know when the Beginner is ready to show me, and I must wait till then.*

When she was satisfied that her smaller plants were healthy and thriving, she walked over to the huge tree with the generous climbing branches and lovingly patted her trunk. The tree responded instantly, shivering a pale pink through the tips of her needles, pleased to be with her friend once again.

"Marbella, my whimsy tree princess," May said through her mind and the touch of her hands, "I see you are still camouflaging the color of your needle points. I miss seeing their bright glow."

"You know I must conceal my lights, May, except at Christmastime when everyone thinks I've been decorated for the season," the tree responded.

"I understand, my princess. Now tell me, what have you seen and heard since last I was here?"

"I have had children play in my boughs again. And they were strong children, with the gift of joy and happiness," Marbella proclaimed.

"These wouldn't happen to be the MacKenzie children from that new family that has moved into town, now would they, Marbella?" asked May with a smile in her voice.

"I believe they are, as Waterford and I have had long discussions about this new MacKenzie clan. We were afraid when Maggie and her family disappeared so suddenly. Why did they leave, May?" Marbella inquired.

May pursed her lips as if she was about to speak aloud, then thought to Marbella, "I'm still trying to sort that one out. I've actually thought I heard their dog, Alice, bark from time to time when I've been inside talking to

Waterford. Now tell me about the pointer pairs you've seen lately."

May stood there talking with the whimsy tree for a while longer, then slipped inside Waterford to discuss the goings on in Waters End. As they talked, she walked through his rooms, looking for any clue she may have missed before. Both satisfied and dissatisfied that she could find no other reason for the disappearance of Maggie and her family, May left Waterford as unobtrusively as she had arrived.

A Pointer Pact

Once May drove away, two cloaked figures materialized from the shrubbery by Waterford's back gate and began walking toward the mean house.

"There she goes again," said Hither slyly to his pointer pair, Yon. "Do you think she spotted us?"

"No, she would have spoken to us," replied Yon. "She has a list of questions a mile long, and the saddest part is that even we together cannot answer them all."

"It's like the whimsy revolt never ended, isn't it?" asked Hither. "I mean, I keep seeing that night and the fires. You warned me this could happen, and still I could not believe it when it did."

"We've had to cross the seas at least a dozen times, and I still get seasick," replied Yon. "And all because of that evil Lord Sebastian MacKenzie cutting Whimsies out of season and without permission. When I tried to warn the trine sprite Princess Toral, she would believe none of it. And now she wants us to find a way to get the missing MacKenzie family back to Waters End."

As they turned the bend and approached the mean house, hither sneered, "There's Lord Ailbert for you."

"Old Bertie, you mean. What of him?" Yon motioned with a tilt of his head.

"His majesty!" Hither exclaimed. "You'd think his pride would have come down a notch or two in the last hundred years or so. Not one of his builder's offspring has amounted to much. And if it wasn't for his own ability to run himself, he would be looking worse than old Ford."

"That house is cursed. That is true," replied Yon. "If only we had told Arian, the trine sprite queen. She might have convinced

Princess Toral that foul play was afoot. Maybe then this could have all been avoided."

"True," replied Hither. "And if you remember, the queen was away at the time. I cannot see the future as you can. Is it possible for old Bertie here to be tamed?"

"Yes," replied Yon. "That is one of the futures I have foreseen. But come along now, we need to remove the dead cat from under the back porch. That new MacKenzie family figured out what it was yesterday, and old Bertie here is so sick, he doesn't have the decency to cover up the smell of his latest kill."

Δ Δ Δ

As Hither and Yon walked behind the mean house, another pointer pair approached Lord Ailbert, speaking quietly amongst themselves.

"Tell me why we are here again?" asked Dither.

"I told Yon we'd meet them beneath the mound behind Lord Ailbert," replied Dawn with impatience.

Confused, Dither asked, "Why don't we meet them at the peak as usual?"

"Because Yon said he had some business to attend to here, and since we were visiting the royal dolphins this evening, it's more convenient to meet here. Besides, I don't know if Hither and Yon want to tell the other pairs their plans quite yet. It seems Blither and Boast are causing problems again, along with Waste-Not and Want-Not."

"How can Waste-Not and Want-Not be causing problems?" inquired Dither.

As they made their way to the back of Lord Ailbert, Dawn replied, "Because they're striving for balance and not getting their way lately. Come on, let's see what the meeting's about."

When they reached the mound at the end of the property, Dawn tapped on an old rusted metal door. Once opened, the door revealed a long, torch-lit stairway leading steeply down to a large room filled with candlelight and fine old wooden chairs and benches placed on thick, brightly-colored and elaborately-woven rugs.

At the bottom of the stairs they turned to the hall on their left, where an open door and a welcoming fire roared to ease their old bones. Hither and Yon were seated across from each other at the long table. Tall pillar candles burned with brilliance within their crystal frames, reflecting both their own interior light as well the massive fireplace behind them.

Hither greeted them with a question as they entered the room, "What news from the royal dolphin Queen Annika?"

"She is still upset by the disappearance of Ford's missing family, and expected us to have resolved this issue by now," answered Dawn.

Then Dither joined in, "Well, as you know, it goes much deeper than that. Those darn harmony trine ceremonies create unions that never made sense in the first place. I mean, why should a trine sprite care what happens to a human, and why should a royal dolphin care, either? We should all stick to our own kind, I say," he concluded, frustrated with this new age and the changes it had wrought.

"Calm down, both of you," ordered Yon, sighing. "As if we don't already have too much to think about."

"So, I have had a vision that may heal the old wounds. Our role could be risky, and I must swear you to secrecy. Because of this, we can't involve any of the other pairs. Will you swear?" Yon asked Dither and Dawn solemnly.

"Right," Dawn said. "Following the Beginner's rules again, are we?"

"And who else's rules are there to follow?" said Dither. "I mean, do you think the Beginner is real or just a tale of convenience passed down the generations to make us think there is something more than the here and now?"

"Pair Dither, we'll have plenty of time to discuss theology later," said Dawn, shaking his head with a bemused smile on his face.

After Dither and Dawn swore to keep this information secret from the other pairs, Yon explained that in one of his visions each member of this new MacKenzie family would undergo a series of challenges. If any one of them failed, the original MacKenzie family might perish, never again to return to Waters End.

"Well that'd be rather tough luck for Maggie and her family then, wouldn't it?" asked Dither, trying to make light of this news.

Dawn eyed him dourly. "Pair Dither, Maggie is the continuum. Everything begins and ends with her. We need her back. That too has been foretold!"

Dither was none too pleased about being reprimanded by his pair in front of Hither and Yon, but took the rebuff good-naturedly. "Patience is what's needed here most."

Over the course of the next few hours, the two pointer pairs discussed the pros and cons of various outcomes and tried to determine each of their roles in promoting the best of them.

When morning broke, they left Lord Sebastian's cavern and dispersed to their own beds for some long overdue rest.

PART 2 — REMEMBERING

Remembering...it is not always a good thing. And letting go is not easy when the mind remembers too much, especially too much sadness, or too much joy that is now lacking.

This house is unhappy and has definitely not been treated well from the time he was first made. Can you fix a broken house? Can you mend a broken heart? Can such terrible wrongs ever be put to right?

Book One of the Whimsy Tree Tales

BAD NEWS BEAR

The next morning at breakfast, Nelson announced that yesterday evening he had purchased the Edwards' house on Dolphin Court. Instead of receiving the excitement he had expected, his family looked at him glumly.

Carson began toying with his ham and eggs, while Evan just looked down into his cereal bowl, and Marlee appeared distracted by something she was looking at outside the dining room window.

Finally Robyn said, "That's nice dear. Would you care for more coffee before you leave for work?"

Nelson raised his voice in frustration. "No, I would not care for any more coffee before I go! In fact, this family seems so ungrateful for all I do for them that I think I shall go this minute."

"As you wish," said Robyn quietly.

Nelson looked at each of them for some kind of congratulations—or, at the least, interest in his decision. When none was offered, his frustration grew. How could he have lived so long with his family and not really known them? All four of them did not care for his sense of practicality in the slightest.

He got up from the table shaking his head in dismay and went upstairs to get his things and head out to the office.

Once he was gone his family sighed aloud, and Robyn told her children she knew the other night it was too late to change their father's mind when he'd said the mean house was perfect for them.

Marlee asked, "Mom, why wouldn't Dad listen to anything we wanted in a new home? I mean, all four of us told him we didn't like or want that house, and that's the one house he picked out of dozens we've looked at."

"Well dear, he really does think he's doing the best for all of us," she replied. "The trouble is, he can't seem to see beyond a dollar sign these days. Let me try to explain this a little better. You see, a few years ago when all of you were much younger, the economy was pretty shaky, and many people lost their jobs and their homes.

Though you may not remember any of this, one year we didn't even have a real Christmas tree, or lights, or store-bought gifts. My girlfriends and I made gifts for all of you from items we found rummaging through each other's attics and basements."

Carson said, "I remember, Mom. That was a great Christmas. We played games, sang carols, and even made up new words for the songs we couldn't remember. And your friends and their families came over and brought some of the food we ate. I still remember Aunt Suzie's pumpkin pie. Evan and I ate most of it when you weren't looking."

"You mean you ate most of it, Carson," said Evan with a grin as he elbowed Carson in the gut.

Feigning hurt, Carson doubled up, then quickly straightened, laughing. "Well, maybe. But there was a whole bowl of whipped cream next to it, so I wasn't sure how much pie I ate and how much whipped cream."

His mother smiled, remembering how worried she and Nelson had been that Christmas. As she was thinking about how well the next few years had turned out for them, she happened to glance down at her watch. "Oh my!" she exclaimed. "It's almost 9:30, and we need to meet May. Hurry up, let's go!"

Carson, Evan, and Marlee raced upstairs, got their things for the day, and dashed back down to the rental car in the garage.

Evan asked Carson, "Isn't there anything we can do to stop Dad from buying the mean house? If it bit me just for visiting it, what's going to happen to us if we live there for real?"

"I don't know," Carson replied. "Maybe May can help, or Waterford. We've got to talk to both of them, and maybe Mom shouldn't be with us all the time, as she seems to be siding with Dad some."

Marlee sighed. "Remember, we're a family. We've got to stick together here."

To which Evan replied, "Just remember who bit whom, and Mom's first reaction was embarrassment in front of that realtor. So don't forget that we three are also a team. If Mom can't help us, maybe we'll have to help ourselves."

Carson looked at each of his siblings seriously for a moment. He knew Evan and he agreed that the mean house was not where they were meant to end up living, but Marlee, being a girl... He wasn't sure he could trust her to do something their parents might not agree with. Another MacKenzie motto popped into his head: *Wait and watch!* And so he would.

Δ Δ Δ

When the family arrived at May's Best, they were surprised to see May out of her normal uniform and wearing a lightweight plaid skirt, blouse, and sweater.

"What happened to your pink and white apron, May, and your pretty little cap?" Marle asked.

"We're going to the city park today instead of talking here."

Once on the sidewalk outside her café, May turned to Robyn. "Did you know your children have been seeing pointer pairs in town?"

"Well yes, and it's just a game they're playing," Robyn replied. "They told me about it last night. Pointer pairs are another tale from the old country."

May looked at Robyn rather sternly, then slowly shook her head. "They are as real as Waterford, you know," she said as they walked the few blocks toward the park.

Robyn looked confused, then turned to Marlee, her concern mounting. "What's going on here?"

"Sorry, Mom," Marlee replied quickly—and a little contritely. "We didn't want to upset you, and we're still unsure who they really are, or what any of this means."

May looked at the four of them. "Have you never heard the tale of Pointers' Peak, then?" Before they could answer, she asked, "Which tales of the old country do you know, and how did you learn them?"

Evan started counting them on his left hand as he volunteered the answer. "We know the tales of the enchanted house, Pointers' Peak, the trine sprites, the wing snatchers, and the whimsy tree revolt," he finished proudly as he tapped his thumb for five tales.

Carson added, "There was also a tale about the tree cutters who caused the whimsy tree revolt, wasn't there?"

"Shush, Carson," Robyn exclaimed. "Marlee's too young for that tale." She turned to May. "I've told the children most of the tales my great-aunt Maggie told me when I was a little girl."

"And just where was that?" May asked.

"Why, in Oak Grove when she visited us," responded Robyn. "Why does that matter?"

Continuing her questioning, May asked, "When did you see your Maggie last?"

"Years ago, maybe fourteen or so. Let me see, it was before the children were born. I remember Maggie came to Nelson and my wedding, then a year or so later, she came again when I found out I was pregnant with Carson. Funny thing is, we've lost touch. Poor old dear must have passed away, but you'd think someone would have notified us. I've asked our cousins, and no one's heard a word."

"Sounds about right." May nodded her head. "All pieces in the puzzle," she mumbled to herself.

Looking up at Robyn and the children, she said, "You see, our town's Maggie and her family have been missing about that long too. And from what you've said about your Maggie, it is possible that she's the same Maggie that used to live here as well."

Confused, Robyn questioned May. "How could your Maggie be my great-aunt? She was showing her age when last I saw her, and she lived in the old country. She didn't have a home and another family over here. If she did, I would have known. I'm sure of that!"

"Well, that's just another mystery for the moment," said May. "Let's tuck it away and get back to why I've brought you here this morning. So—getting back to the tales you've heard, it seems you haven't heard the tale of the royal dolphins yet, right?"

This time all four of them shook their heads left to right.

"That's what I thought," said May as they turned the corner and walked into the city park. May led them down a winding path bordering the estuary, then along the waterfront till they came to a small cove secluded from view by a shallow dip in the path and a mound covered with wild white gardenia bushes.

The Royal Dolphins

Marlee stopped to smell the fragrant flowers as the others sat down at an old, weathered redwood picnic table on the sand. Some movement caught her attention; she'd spooked what looked to be a hummingbird feeding on a flower. It looked at Marlee quizzically as it fluttered in a hover about a foot from her face, then suddenly took off like a bolt of lightning out over the estuary.

At the picnic table, May produced a thermos of hot tea from a large woven handbag along with cups, sugar, and cream for five. She pulled out some shortbread cookies, placing all on the table neatly with little white paper napkins. "I thought you'd want some refreshment while we waited."

"Waited for what?" Carson almost yelped, so tired was he of more and more questions with one never being answered before a new one had formed.

"For the royal dolphins, of course," replied May. "And seeing as this is one tale none of you have heard yet, perhaps it's time for the telling," she said with a nod of her head. "I think some of what's going on will make more sense to you if you learn more about the beginning of Waters End, and that's where the royal dolphins come in."

Marlee, Evan, and Carson's eyes glowed as Carson pulled out their questions list and added another mystery to it: the royal dolphins. As their mother sat quietly waiting for the story to begin, they looked at each other in anticipation, excited to learn a new piece of information.

Thus May began to tell them about the royal dolphins.

Some time ago, long before you or I existed, one proud race ruled the oceans over all this fine planet. They were known as the peacemakers and guides who helped all cross the great seas to travel from one land to the next. They were wise beyond our ken—kind, practical, and fair in all their dealings with any living creature upon this earth. They were, of course, the royal dolphins.

The royal dolphins have deep lavender-colored topsides and pale lavender undersides. Their length can easily exceed twelve feet, and their noses are more pointed and long, especially as compared to other more common dolphin species. They also have a touch of gold and silver on their snouls.

Like the trine sprites, they live a long time. Unlike the sprites, though, none of them are born into royalty. Instead, they have to earn the privilege of royalty, for the duties that come with that job are neverending, and only the strongest of mind, heart, and spirit in each generation become the king and queen of the seas at any one point in time.

It's easy to tell a king or queen dolphin apart from the other royal dolphins by their top color alone; it is a deep and brilliant amethyst. And they are not chosen by their peers to hold these titles. There is a stronger force at work here, and many of the dolphin kings and queens did not seek the title. However, when their skin color starts to brighten from deep lavender to the more brilliant amethyst, all who behold them know that they have earned the title and been chosen by the Beginner.

It is said that the royal dolphins sense the feelings and needs of those around them. When a ship's crew is hungry, tired or lost, the royal dolphins guide them to where they need to be. And when a ship is on a quest, the royal dolphins appear to know the nature of that quest and assist the ship to reach her port.

Stopping for effect, May looked at each of them, ensuring she had their undivided attention.

You see, it was the royal dolphins who guided Maggie's brother, Captain Jon Dinsmore's ship up the estuary to the town he founded and named Waters End. In fact, Captain Dinsmore named the street he built his home on 'Dolphin Court' for this very reason.

May looked up to see surprise on all their faces, and she wondered, should she tell the rest of the tale yet or save it for later? While she was trying to decide, these questions were taken out of her mind as Marlee screeched excitedly and ran to the water's edge, going in up to her waist when the most beautiful large amethyst colored dolphin swam within a few feet of the shoreline. Right behind her came Carson and Evan, as all three swam around this magnificent creature.

Calmly, May stood up and walked over to the water line. Lifting her face up and raising her voice in a pealing, keening manner, she emitted clicking sounds that shocked the family. In response, the King of the Sea raised his head, nickering back at May in a language none of the MacKenzies could understand. Then the two of them settled down to a series of back and forths in this same strange language. At one point, it appeared they were laughing—at another, almost crying.

Finally, May turned to the MacKenzies. "I present to you King Koru, High Lord and Protector of all the oceans on this planet. I have already introduced him to you, and he is pleased to learn of your existence."

Stunned beyond measure, yet so elated to hear about and then *meet* a royal dolphin, Robyn was temporarily spellbound.

Recovering from the shock of realizing that May's current tale was true and real, just like the pointer pairs and Waterford, she said, "May! Who are you? How do you know all this, and how can this all be real?"

May gave Robyn a slow, knowing smile. "Soon I will answer those questions. For the moment, let us bid farewell to King Koru, for he must return to the open sea."

Carson, Evan, and Marlee walked up the beach dripping wet and smiling wider than their mother had ever seen. They all waved to King Koru as he swam out into the channel and made his way swiftly out to the open sea.

Then Carson pulled out their questions list from his back pocket to find all the ink had run and he would have to create a new list, and they laughed, as they were still so happy to have met and swum with a royal dolphin.

Though their tea had grown quite cold by then, May produced a fresh thermos of hot tea as they sat once more at the picnic table to discuss what to do next.

Robyn blurted out, "May! We need some information. Was it your objective to help us today or to shock us?"

A bit put off, May looked at them and casually shrugged her shoulders. "Well, it was Marlee who called the dolphin just now, not I."

"But I didn't do anything!" exclaimed Marlee in confusion.

"Hmmm," replied May, "did you not stop to smell the wild gardenias and talk to a hummerling before we sat down to our tea?" she asked slyly.

"If you mean did I see a hummingbird? Why yes, I did," replied Marlee.

"Well, there are hummingbirds, and then there are hummerlings," replied May. "Though related, they are not the same. Hummingbirds are a tad smaller and cannot change colors to match their environment, nor do they have golden beaks, and more importantly, they do not have the gift of universal speech. Only the hummerlings do."

May shrugged her shoulders. "No, there is so much you don't understand yet—so much more you need to know, and though I've no proof, I truly believe you are related to my Maggie somehow. King Koru believes this as well, and I don't know how this could be. I thought I knew Maggie quite well. You see, we're related. I am descended from Fiona, the Lady Margaret's niece, so I should have known of your existence...all of you, and yet I did not!"

Robyn looked at May a bit skeptically, then tentatively asked, "Does this mean you have some trine sprite in you as well? I ask because the tale of the enchanted house says that Maggie's niece Fiona was said to be part trine sprite herself."

"How astute of you, Robyn," replied May cautiously. "Yes, I suppose I do, then." May quickly changed the subject by saying, "So, here's my current plan. First, is there any way to stop Mr. MacKenzie from moving into the Edwards home?"

Robyn shook her head. "There is no changing his mind once it's made up."

"Not what I wanted to hear," May replied sadly. "So, on to Plan B. We must find the pointer pair named Hither and Yon."

Finally Robyn felt less out of control, for she had heard of these two pointers from her great-aunt's tales. "But don't we need to get to a place called Pointers' Peak to call them?"

"Yes," replied May. "And that is not an easy task, as the only one I know of is in the old country!"

"But if we are seeing pointers here and now," said Carson, "they must have another meeting place."

"Perhaps, Carson. Perhaps," replied May. "I hadn't thought of that. I wonder if they are meeting above the old Indian burial grounds beyond the north side of town. That is the highest peak in the area, and it juts out over and above the estuary. There have been some tragic accidents over the years up there, as it has a sharp bend in the old dirt road near the top."

As they walked back to May's café, May turned and stopped in front of them. "There is one other thing you should know about the royal dolphins and the pointer pairs. You see, it is also said that the pointer named Yon told the royal dolphins to stop here at Waters End, for Yon had foreseen this as the town where the damage done to the whimsy trees by Lord Sebastian would be healed."

Sighing, Robyn said, "I think I've heard and seen more than I can handle in one day. I've got some errands to run for Nelson this afternoon, as we will be moving into our new home as soon as Mr. Edwards moves out."

Turning to her children, Robyn asked if they were okay.

Marlee spoke first. "Mom, maybe it's because we've heard these stories our whole lives. For us, it's exciting to find they're true. Maybe it's harder for you to accept because you're all grown up?"

In response, Robyn hugged Marlee and promised she would try not to put her own fears onto Marlee and her brothers.

Δ Δ Δ

As soon as their mom was gone, Carson turned to May and asked where the old Indian burial grounds were located.

May told them it was too soon to think of locating the modern day Pointers' Peak. She encouraged them to get their questions list together and think each question through carefully before asking, because the pointers were notorious for answering one question with another.

May left them with a warning. "A pointer's passion usually bodes ill for sprites and humans alike. Now, I've some investigating to do myself and may be gone a few days. Wait for my return."

Δ Δ Δ

That evening, once their parents had gone to bed, Carson started a new list of questions. Turning to Evan and Marlee, he said, "Let's recreate our list and see if we can make sense of what's going on here."

Together they came up with:

1. Were Ford and the mean house actually made from the whimsy trees?

2. How to find Pointers' Peak and call Hither and Yon?

3. How could their Maggie be the same Maggie from Ford's missing family?

4. If May is related to Fiona, does she have any special trine sprite powers?

5. How to survive the mean house?

"That's a good start," Marlee yawned.

Nodding in agreement, Evan added, "Let's visit Waterford again tomorrow. I bet he can help us more with our list."

Satisfied with their plan, they fell asleep dreaming of hummerlings, royal dolphins, pointer pairs, and Ford's missing family.

A Crystal Prism

When Carson, Evan, and Marlee came down to breakfast the next morning, their mother and father were deep in discussion going over their to-do list for moving into their new home. Because they were not interested in their parents' list, the kids ordered breakfast and once again reviewed their own list.

Their father looked up after they had ordered and smiled. He apologized for being upset with them the morning before, and reminded them at the same time that this was all for their own good.

"That's okay, Dad," Marlee said. "We understand, and we do appreciate what you're doing for us, don't we?" she finished, looking meaningfully at both her brothers.

"Yes, Dad," said Carson. "Football tryouts start soon, and I need to practice."

"Mr. Edwards is moving out tomorrow, and our new home is being cleaned the day after," Nelson responded. "This means we'll be moving in this week. Perhaps you could begin practicing your catches and throws with Evan in the park today? Maybe you'll meet some of the local children as well," he beamed, as he himself was looking forward to being more organized once again.

"That sounds coolio, Dad," replied Carson, though for once he could care less about sports.

Δ Δ Δ

After their father had left and their mother went out to run more errands, they visited Waterford. Not wanting to get any closer than necessary, they passed the mean house from the opposite side of the street. They could see that Mr. Edwards was packing, as boxes were strewn all over the front yard, and the garage door was open and full of furniture and movers adding even more boxes.

Marlee let out a huge sigh of relief once they turned the bend in the road and saw Waterford at the end of Dolphin Court. All three of them dashed across the empty street and ran through Waterford's back gate and sat on the rear lawn facing him.

"Hi, Ford!" exclaimed Marlee happily. "How are you today?"

"Hmmm..." replied Ford sleepily. "You didn't visit me yesterday, and I get drowsy when I have no one to talk to. Any news of my missing family?" he asked hopefully.

Shaking his head for no, Carson spoke first about meeting the royal dolphin, King Koru. Then Evan pointed out that they got to swim with him, and Marlee added that King Koru and May thought that both their families were somehow related to Ford's missing Maggie and her family.

"Well, well!" exclaimed Ford. "And the best part is learning that you are virtually family. Maybe you will move in with me, then?" he inquired happily, and proceeded to smile as only a house can do by slightly lifting up his windows at the outside edges.

"Oh, Ford," Marlee sighed. "We can't, as Dad's bought the mean house and we move into it in just a few days. We are all so worried and sad that we don't get to move into you instead."

Before Ford could reply, Evan said, "But we'll be living closer to you now, so we'll visit you all the time. We don't want you to be lonely."

"Ahh..." sighed Waterford. "I was so hoping you could move in and keep me company."

Then Marlee asked, "Ford, what do you look like on the other side?"

"Hmmm... I forgot, you haven't come indoors before, have you?"

"No," said Marlee politely, "and we'd really like to, if that's okay with you."

Ford asked them to come up on his rear porch and unlocked his back door so they could come inside. "It is usually more proper for visitors to enter through my front door, but seeing as we're related, perhaps you won't mind entering through the family room."

As they walked up on Ford's rear deck, he opened wide a pair of French doors encased in aged wooden frames that had grayed over time.

Marlee exclaimed, "Why, Ford! You are beautiful inside. Everything is so clean and neat, and there's no dust anywhere. How come you don't fix the broken windows on your face?"

"I've let the windows stay broken because I've been so sad without my family, but maybe I'll fix them now, seeing as you'll be visiting me more often."

"Yes, do that," said Carson. "Then we can hang out with you when we need to get away from the mean house."

"Sigh... You mean Lord Ailbert, don't you?" replied Waterford.

"So he has a name, too?" asked Evan.

"Yes," replied Ford. "And for years we other houses have thought him rather pompous because of it. There was a time when he wasn't so full of himself, but that was long ago. I used to call him Bertie then, just as he called me Ford."

Then Carson changed the subject, as he couldn't imagine calling the mean house anything other than mean. "Ford, we've been building our questions list and wonder if you can help us with it."

So they reviewed their questions of the prior night and waited patiently for Ford to answer. After what seemed like a long time, he said, "We might be made from the whimsy trees. Have you asked May that question? If anyone knows, she will, but as I said before, the other houses think I'm silly when I mention this. They believe we were made by something more powerful than a tree, and I don't think they know any of the old tales, either."

Then he thought for a while longer, and as he did, the children walked around looking in his various rooms, trying out his fine, dark-wood furniture so nicely covered in soft and inviting fabrics.

As Marlee was admiring an old etched mirror in what looked to have been a study, she thought she saw something move from the corner of her eye. As she turned, she saw a beautiful crystal prism hanging by a window and glowing in many colors as it caught the morning sunlight. What she couldn't understand though was what made it turn, as no windows were open in this part of the house. She walked slowly up to it and thought she saw a dog's smiling face.

Quickly she blinked her eyes, rubbed them vigorously with the backs of her hands, then looked again. This time the prism was not moving and she saw only its reflected colors. Confused, she wondered if that had been a dog's face or her imagination.

"Ford," Marlee thought, "what did your dog Alice look like?"

"She was fluffy, with a white undercoat and black-and-silver top coat, and she had a tail that curled up when she walked. She always looked like she was smiling, even when she was up to no good," replied Ford. "Why do you ask, young Marlee?"

Marlee replied that she was just curious, then she asked Waterford about the prism by the window. He answered that he didn't remember it being there, but he'd been so upset at losing his family that he hadn't been as tidy as he used to be.

Carson and Evan walked in, and the four of them discussed the beautiful crystal prism that Ford had not remembered being there before. Then Carson added it as another curiosity to their list.

Out loud, Marlee asked, "Ford, are there any other things you don't remember being in you or on you before your family disappeared?"

"Hmmm..." he pondered. "Maybe we should look for things each time you come to visit. May has been looking, and she thought she heard Alice bark once from a long ways away."

"Right," said Carson. "Now we have something we can do that makes sense. Ford, do you have any writing paper and a pen? We're going to need to write down things as we find them, then figure out what else you do or don't remember."

"Ya," said Evan. "We'll be like detectives." He smiled as he started looking around the rest of the room and holding up objects for Ford to inspect; first a letter opener, then a glass paperweight, followed by a fountain pen. To each he received a 'no' from Ford, but he wasn't daunted in the least.

After spending a while longer walking through Ford and not finding anything else Ford was unfamiliar with, they realized it was getting late and it was time to go.

EDWARD EDWARDS

As the MacKenzie children were leaving Waterford, Edward Edwards was taking a soon-to-be-final walk through the neighborhood he had spent his entire life in. Deep in thought, he almost ran into them, then recovered at the last minute and stood behind a tree as they passed him by, absorbed in their own conversation.

Once they were gone he breathed a sigh of relief. He knew they were the new MacKenzie children who would be moving into his home, and he hated them for that. *But what was that they were saying?* He asked himself. *Something about the old house talking to them?*

Edward stood by the bush, confused. He'd heard similar stories before and had always laughed at them. Now, as he was losing his home, he wasn't so certain.

As he looked up at the old house with the broken windows, he smiled a cruel smile, knowing that he had been the one to break those windows many years before.

Just then his memory jolted him with Kyle's old taunt of "Hey Ed-Ed-Ed-w-w-wards!" and he was enraged yet again. In his mind, everything went back to that one tease from Kyle MacKenzie, and Edward was filled once more with anger and resentment against this house and its family. He did not remember any of the jibes and taunts he had flung at the other MacKenzie children over the years. He only remembered Kyle's one taunt. In his mind, anything he ever did was justified. Whomever he did it to deserved it.

In this state of agitation, he quickly walked back to the only home he had ever known. Once inside, he went down into the basement and looked once more for the journals his wife's diary had mentioned.

Finding her diary had been quite by accident, as he did not know she even kept one, and he would not have found it this week at all had he not lost his job at the Bingham Company and been forced to sell his home. While sorting through old books and papers, he came upon his wife's handwriting. He knew it was hers instantly for the script was rather large, with sloppily-formed characters that tilted both up and down on a page.

More anger seeped into him, as by dying, his wife had forced him to lose his family and finally his home. She had never been considerate of his needs and wants. Selfish— yes she had been that, and unkind as well. To think he had brought her home from college and shared his marvelous family home with her.

There was no way he could raise their four children and work a full-time job at the same time all on his own. The sitters he had tried to employ never lasted more than a day or so... They tried to tell him his home was haunted or some such bunk. *No,* he thought. His dead wife was also to blame for his losing his family, his job, and now his home.

Though normally meticulous, Edward began tearing through old boxes, tossing their contents left and right, paying no attention to where or how they fell once they left his grasp.

About an hour later, he finally discovered an old tin box in the bottom of a large trunk shoved up under an eve in the back of the basement. The box had faded colors on it from what must have been a painting of some sort at one time. As he tried to lift the lid, he noted a lock that prevented him from doing so. He wiggled the lock to no effect, then sifted through the remainder of the trunk looking for a key.

When none was found, he picked up an old silver candlestick from inside the trunk and slammed it at the lock, breaking it in two almost instantly. It felt good to break the lock, and some of the tension began to seep out of him as he slowly lifted the lid.

Inside he saw multiple small, old books, some loose papers, and sketches. Reaching for the first book, a large, dark spider jumped on the back of his hand and bit him. "Ow!" he yelled as he smashed one of the books onto the spider, killing it instantly. Then, in his surprise at being bitten, he dropped the book back into the tin box along with the dead spider.

Quickly he carried the entire box upstairs to the kitchen counter. After tending to his hand, he took out a pair of cooking tongs to lift the remaining items out of the box and onto the kitchen table.

"What have we here?" he spoke aloud, though no one else was present. "Looks like I have five books, each slightly older than the last, with the bottom one being the most frayed and tattered of them all."

Pensively he sifted through the limply bound pages and sketches, looking for anything of meaning. He found the original drawings of a house floor plan, and under it were the words *Lord Ailbert.* In the top right corner were other words that made no sense to him. "Lord Sebastian MacKenzie's new home," he mouthed. The odd thing was that the floor plan resembled his home, confusing him, as this had always been the Edwards family home not a MacKenzie home.

Edward cringed as it occurred to him that a MacKenzie may have built his home and lived here for some time. Then he found several old bills of lading with expenses listed for various items having to do with the building of a house a long time ago. The script was rough and mostly faded, yet he could make out enough of it to know that these also belonged to his home.

As he took the last papers out of the box, he came upon a land title of some sort. Reading more carefully, he could make out the words *Silver Mine Site Plan*, and a map sketching a proposed location over by the old Indian burial grounds. Then he saw the spider he had killed scurry up and away under a kitchen cabinet. This made even less sense than the contents of the box, and though he thought of going after the spider, he knew it was useless.

Good riddance, he thought, forgetting about and dropping the papers back into the box. *Let him bite one of the MacKenzies and see how they like it,* he chuckled, as the notion amused him. Truth was, his hand was starting to sting rather badly, and he saw the back of his hand changing color and beginning to swell as well.

Returning to the kitchen table, he attempted to ignore his hand as he slowly opened the newest book first. The script was clean and neatly written, and he knew it was his mother's writing. He smiled remembering her and missing her at the same time. She was the only person who had ever been kind to him. He knew his father's meanness had killed her long before her time, but he got back at the old man in the end by returning the favor and being just as rude and unkind to his father during his final years.

Edward sighed as he remembered his mother's love, the only true love he'd ever received, then slowly he began scanning the contents of her diary.

Edward turned five today. I bought him some new clothes and the stuffed teddy bear he wanted. He is already such a solemn child, never asking for anything the way other children do. I wish I could have provided him with siblings to play with, but it appears that wasn't part of God's plan for us.

I am beginning to fear for my life, just as some of my predecessors have. If Edward ever finds my journal, I hope he will realize that it is this house that has made his father cruel. I do not know how much more of either I can take, and sometimes Lord Ailbert will not listen even to me.

Why, just the other night when we had some important guests to dinner, the house closed the entrance to the kitchen just as our maid Lucinda was beginning to serve the main course. It took me forever to cajole Lord Ailbert into letting Lucinda finish her task. Thankfully, our guests thought my fib about Lucinda receiving news of a sick family member only interrupted her cooking and serving tasks temporarily.

I have found some old journals from women who have lived here before me. I am quite upset, as it appears that this house is cursed, and so are its inhabitants. I do my best to make sure Lord Ailbert is taken care of properly. I have schooled Edward to put away his things neatly and in a timely manner so as not to offend the house further. I also have not told Edward about Lord Ailbert. In exchange, the house has promised to leave Edward alone and not hurt him.

At this point, Edward could read no more of his mother's journal. He was stunned to learn he had been raised in a living house. Gently placing his mother's journal aside, he picked up the oldest journal with the most frayed edges. As he opened this book, the first page crumbled in his hand, making him careful with all of the subsequent pages as he began to read what looked to be a woman named Elizabeth's journal.

The Legacy

I have done my best, though I fear greatly I will be damned for it. Someone had to take control, as this blasted house will only respond to one master at a time. My three younger sisters were too weak to ever control Lord Ailbert, and my parents were getting senile in their old age, drooling at the dining room table, and in general, disgusting me at every turn.

How was I to ever find a suitable husband living in these conditions? And I so wanted to marry my Mr. Edwards. To do so, I knew I had to bring a decent dowry with me to entice him. Therefore I could not split the house with my sisters. I really had no choice in the matter.

I still can't believe my father insisted on being called Lord Sebastian MacKenzie. Our cousins, the other MacKenzie family, do not insist on such titles, and they look to be far happier and wealthier than we have ever been. It isn't fair, I say.

Oh, I curse my father for cutting the rotten whimsy trees out of season and building this monster of a home. Even I can only survive by becoming more and more devious than Lord Ailbert, for I must out-think him at every turn, lest he no longer do my bidding.

From as far back as I can remember I have held a battle of wills with old Bertie here, though he hates it when I call him thus. Why couldn't he have had a sense of humor like some of the other houses on Dolphin Court? From what I can tell, they do as they're told and do not play tricks on their owners.

Some of Bertie's tricks are not terrible, yet it is disconcerting to have guests over only to have them become trapped in the loo, or bitten by mosquitoes when the windows refuse to stay shut at dusk.

Yes, I may be damned for it, but I saw to it that my parents' carriage could not make the narrow turn in the road just below the old Indian burial grounds. I loosed the cart harness just enough to have it give way in a tight corner. Their carriage left the road and tipped over the cliff above the estuary. Though I appear to be crying to the constable and local townsfolk, I am so glad to be rid of them. It has been three days now and still their bodies have not been recovered.

My three sisters have now disappeared as well. I have told everyone that they went abroad to find husbands of their own now that I am engaged to the most eligible bachelor in all of Waters End. It is good that Lord Ailbert can clean up his messes, as I told him I did not want to smell any decaying bodies after he suffocated them while they slept last week.

And tonight, as I sit in my glorious new sitting room which will be off-limits even to my future husband, I can't help but wonder if I could have managed this differently, if there were any other choices than the ones I've made.

Slowly and with true amazement, Edward closed his long-lost relative's journal. Though tempted to read more of it and to look through the others from the box, he needed to gain a sense of what this all meant. To learn only now the value of his heritage and to be losing it to another family of MacKenzies. The irony of it was more than he could take in at the moment.

Time—he needed time to think, and to plan his revenge. The one thing he knew was that he needed to find a way to repossess his family home. If his long-lost relative Elizabeth could kill to keep it hers, then maybe, so could he.

MOVING DAY

Nothing eventful happened over the next few days. Carson, Evan, and Marlee continued to look for pointers and saw none. They also returned to the park hoping to see the royal dolphin King Koru again, with no luck. Marlee even stopped to smell the wild gardenias, but no hummerling appeared this time.

When they went by May's Best, they were told she was out of town until the weekend. With nothing else to do, they visited Ford each day and continued searching for more items he might not have noticed before. Evan found a paperclip on one of the steps leading up to the two third-floor bedrooms, and it appeared that would be it until Carson found a dog collar in the room with the crystal prism hanging by the window.

He'd been crawling around the floor on his hands and knees, trying to best Evan's silly paperclip when his hand bumped into something under the loveseat by the telephone table.

"Ford," Carson asked, "is this your missing dog Alice's dog collar?"

"Is it pink or gray?" asked Waterford.

"Guess again," Carson laughed, still holding the collar up. Then a thought struck him. "Ford, are you color-blind?"

"If you mean do I know what colors are, then no, I'm not. But I've never paid much attention to what they look like."

"Ah-ha!" said Evan as he picked up a brightly-colored throw pillow from the loveseat and asked Ford what colors were on the pillow.

"Green and pink?" Ford responded hesitantly.

"Oh Ford," sighed Marlee. "You are color-blind."

When Waterford didn't respond, Carson gently patted Waterford's wall by the window. "It's okay, Ford—you don't have to see colors. But what about this dog collar?"

"It could belong to Alice, but why is it in this room and Alice isn't?"

Dashing to a table in Ford's family room, Evan quickly returned with their list and proudly added Alice's dog collar as a second item Ford did not remember being in him when his family went missing.

"That's two things now, Ford—the crystal prism and Alice's dog collar," he said. "And both found in this same room. If we find a third item here in the study..."

"I get it, Evan," Marlee commented. "There is something strange about this room."

As they were saying farewell to Ford on this last day before they moved, they decided to climb the large tree in the backyard once more. Just as before, as Marlee approached the lowest branch it was too high for her to reach, yet as she got closer she saw it actually lower itself for her to grab hold of and hoist herself up.

"Ford," Marlee thought, "did this tree just lower its branch for me?"

In her mind she heard Ford say, "Why yes, little Marlee."

She smiled wide and sweetly, as nothing was surprising her about Water's End anymore. Then she proceeded to climb the tree and join her brothers at the top.

Book One of the Whimsy Tree Tales

Marlee's Nightmare

The move into the mean house was uneventful. Carson, Evan, and Marlee got the rooms they had thought would be theirs. In between putting their things away, all three of them spent some time gazing out of Evan's window at the mound in the backyard, hoping a pointer would appear—but nothing.

That first night their father ordered a pizza and salads from the local pizza shop, and everyone went to bed rather early, as they were tired from lifting and carrying boxes and unpacking all day.

About two hours later, Robyn was rudely awakened by a shout.

"Mom!" yelled Evan as he dashed into his parents' new bedroom.

Robyn sluggishly looked up, mumbling, "What?"

"Marlee's having a nightmare and we can't wake her!" exclaimed Evan, full of concern. "Come quick! We need your help!"

Nelson rolled over from his side of the bed and flopped his pillow on top of his head. "Oh no, not again. I need my sleep."

Robyn responded with, "I'll handle this, dear," as she grabbed her robe and walked down the hall to find Carson trying to shake Marlee awake.

"Carson, that technique won't work. Grab me a glass of water from the bathroom, please." Just as Robyn said that, Marlee sat straight up in bed with her eyes wide open and let out a scratchy, high-pitched scream. Then she fell back onto the bed as if dead.

"Yikes! She's never done that before," wailed Evan.

Robyn placed her fingers on Marlee's throat to check for a pulse. Finding it good and strong, she sighed heavily and began to rub Marlee's arms gently, trying to soothe her.

Slowly Marlee opened her eyes, but they appeared to be out of focus. Then she sat up and threw her arms around her mom and began sobbing hysterically till she started to hiccup.

"What were you dreaming?" Carson asked.

"Are you okay, kiddo?" inquired Evan softly from the foot of the bed.

Wearily, Marlee shook her head. "I don't want to talk about it, and I'm starting to forget already. Something was taking the air out of me. I couldn't breathe, then all of a sudden it stopped. Maybe that's when you came in?"

"It's okay now," her mother soothed. "You know, this always happens to you when we move into a new house. But I've got to say, this is the worst nightmare you've ever had."

"I'll say, as I never felt like a house was trying to kill me before," replied Marlee.

"Is that what it was?" asked Carson as he sat down next to her and patted her hand.

"Why, I guess so." Marlee looked at them with uncertainty as a new fear entered her mind. Both Carson and Evan knew at once that this was something the house had actually caused.

Then Evan said, "She's okay, Mom. Carson and I will both stay with her tonight."

Robyn looked at the three of them and was so thankful they could support each other at times like these. She'd never had siblings, and always wanted one. Where she'd been alone, they would never be. She smiled. "Hey! What about a story to take our minds off of things?"

"Good idea, Mom," replied Evan. "Tell Marlee's favorite. You know, the one about the faeries."

"Sprites!" chided Marlee. "And they're called trine sprites, stupid!"

"Hah!" said Evan. "Thought that would get you going!" And he smiled, as it was good to see Marlee being fearless again.

Sighing and smiling as well, their mother said, "Let's all get in bed with Marlee and cuddle up for this tale." So all three snuggled together with Marlee and their mom in the middle of Marlee's pink-and-white, queen-sized bed.

"Let me see, where to begin. Ah! I think I'll tell the one about the harmony trine ceremony, seeing as you three have formed your own sort of trine, and because we now know that Waterford is a real, living house, and we've met a royal dolphin, and you three seem to think you've seen pointers in the area."

"And don't forget about the mean house, Mom," said Evan quickly. "Even if he hasn't talked to us yet, it did bite me the first day we came here."

Book One of the Whimsy Tree Tales

"Now Evan, you know you only got a splinter in your hand that day," their mother chided, though her eyes betrayed her. All three children could see the worry there, so they knew she was wondering about Marlee's nightmare as well.

Clearing her throat, Robyn began telling them about harmony trines.

Sprites in Trine

As you may remember from the Tale of the Enchanted House, the trine sprites were similar to the common everyday water faery with a few exceptions. They are said to live for a long time, baring the occasional accident, or death by a wing snatcher. They are friendly for the most part, but cautious around and sometimes even deadly to humans.

A trine sprite is a most curious creature in that they are born individuals, and often bond in threesomes, which is partly where their name comes from, as a trine represents a balance of peace and trust, which creates a third element: action.

Stopping for a moment to make a point, Robyn explained, "You see, when we feel peaceful inside and trust our instincts—that is, when we trust our intuition—we can do things more easily than when we don't feel this way. It's kind of like when you play football, Carson. It's like the days when you received a solid catch, and dodged the other team members so easily that when you reached the goal post, you knew this was the only outcome from the minute you got the ball."

As Carson grinned, Marlee said, "For me it's like running. When I competed in track at our last school, I won when I was happy, and running usually makes me happy."

"Yes, dear," replied their mother. "It can be as simple as that. Now imagine that you have two really good friends, and that when you are with them you can sometimes feel even better and do even more. That's what it's like to be one of a trine."

As Marlee and her brothers started discussing this concept, their mother said, "Now, getting back to the story..."

This trine bonding usually occurred shortly before or after the sprites became independent from their fathers and mothers. But for some it did not occur until much later in life. Think of it as you three being sister and brothers, for the bonding is an eternal friendship that transcends your future spouse, friends, and children. In many cases, a trine can even transcend siblings.

The harmony trine, as the friendship ceremony was referred to, usually occurred during the festival of the fall equinox. It occurred in the fall because that is the time when crops were harvested. It's symbolized by a bond so strong that it could stand the test of time and still bear fruit. So the trine sprites have family, friends, and then an extended family whose members are part of their special harmony trine.

To each they shared loyalty, to each they were friends for life, and to each they gave love and support. How else does one live 500 years or more unless their backbone is strong, unless their support system is in place?

It has also been said that sometimes a trine sprite will bond with an outsider. Though this is quite rare, when it does occur, a special sharing of strengths transpires. It is said that the trine sprites live as long as they do because somewhere, back in time, some of them bonded with their whimsy trees. Or is it that the whimsies live so long because they bonded with their trine sprites? It can get rather confusing, as we don't really know who lived longest first.

Also, both the whimsies and the trine sprites are said to be the direct descendants of the Beginner of Us All. Just who or what this Beginner of theirs is supposed to be, we do not know, but I assume it is something akin to our one God.

If you remember the tale of the enchanted house, you might remember that Toral was a trine sprite princess. It is said that her harmony trine was the most unusual of all, in that it consisted of a human and a fish. Maggie never told me which human or what type of fish, but after hearing May tell of the royal dolphin and meeting King Koru, I am beginning to think a royal dolphin must have been one member her trine.

Also, trine sprites were said to be hard workers; taking care of their whimsy trees was only one of their sacred duties. And as you know, they play as hard as they work, and they love both music and practical jokes. But never tease a trine sprite in return, for their skins are rather thin, and they don't take to teasing as well as we do. Trine sprites have fun, but seldom laugh aloud like you and I. They hold their merriment inside, and a smile is usually the best you can expect when something really tickles them.

Robyn sighed, then continued, "I don't know what else to tell you about harmony trines or the trine sprites themselves without going into the tale of the whimsy tree revolt. And after the night we've just had, that would not be a good idea, don't you think?"

"But Mom," wailed Evan, "that would explain things so much better. I mean, why the mean house is so mean, and maybe that would help—not hurt—Marlee's nightmares."

"Now Evan, I can't believe our new home is evil. We moved in just fine today. We've had no problems at all, and Mr. Edwards left the house so clean and tidy. I haven't found a speck of dust or dirt anywhere, even in the basement."

"But Mom," Carson said, "you don't get it. This wasn't a normal Marlee-mare. She was being strangled by this house!"

"Now that is quite enough, Carson. I think we all need to get some sleep now. Marlee, do you feel any better?"

"Yes Mama, and I'll be okay as long as Carson and Evan sleep with me tonight."

"Well, I could sleep with you instead, little one."

"No, Mama. I want to be with my brothers. Besides, we are our own trine for the moment—until we grow up, that is."

Though Robyn's heartstrings were pulling on her with worry, she only said, "Oh, okay. Now to bed, then—all three of you. Call me if you need me," she said as she cautiously left the room.

"Sheesh!" uttered Carson the minute she was gone. "Marlee, do you understand now that Mom just doesn't get it?"

"Ya, Carson. I'm beginning to. I was so terrified in that dream," Marlee whispered softly, as if afraid to say it too loudly.

Evan looked at her and whispered, "Do you think the house is hearing everything we say?" Both Carson and Marlee fell silent as they understood what might be happening.

Then Carson whispered back, "Let's take a walk in the morning while Mom's making breakfast. We can talk more freely then, okay?"

Marlee and Evan nodded their heads, then the three of them pulled up the covers and tried to go to sleep—which they did eventually, and nothing else happened that first night in their new home.

Δ Δ Δ

While the children slept, their new home, Lord Ailbert, was wide awake. "Hmmm," he was muttering quietly to himself, "who are these new children living inside me? They are not like any other children who have lived here before, nor are their parents. Not only have they not commanded me to do anything yet, they appear to care for each other so strongly. This is so unusual. I wonder if I was ever cared for the way they care for each other..."

Then Lord Ailbert tried to remember, and in the trying, he too fell asleep for the night.

BACON AND EGGS

The next morning dawned clear and sunny, though there was just a hint of fall cooling in the air. All three MacKenzie children were up and dressed before their mother was even awake, so they left a note on Marlee's bed saying they were taking a walk around the neighborhood and would be back in time for breakfast.

They made a beeline for Waterford and were silent as they walked the length of houses around the bend in the road to get there. As usual, they walked in through the gate to the rear yard, then approached the back porch door just in time to hear a click as Ford unlocked it for them to enter.

Evan quickly recounted Marlee's nightmare to Ford while they sat in the family room's big overstuffed furniture. As he finished, they felt the house begin to shake, and Marlee actually fell out of her seat and onto the floor, letting out a big, "Ouch, Ford!"

"Oh, sorry," Ford replied absentmindedly. "Your news has made me angry. Old Bertie needs a talking to. I need to discuss his behavior with the other houses right now. Can you come back in a bit? We've got to come up with a plan, as this is unacceptable, little Marlee."

As Marlee brushed down her backside, Carson said, "Before or after lunch, Ford?"

"Oh, after," Ford replied. He was clearly rather distracted, as his voice already sounded far away.

Tale of The Whimsy Tree Revolt

They felt better on the walk home, as they knew—well, they hoped—Ford would figure something out. When they walked into the kitchen, they kissed their mother good morning, and then Marlee asked if she would tell them about the whimsy revolt.

"Why Marlee," she replied, "I didn't know you liked that particular story. Why the sudden interest?"

"We just want to understand more about how the family from Waterglenn disappeared."

"What makes you think the whimsies had anything to do with the disappearance of the Waterglenn family?" her mother inquired.

"It's just a theory, Mom. Can you tell us that story now, paleeeease!" Evan almost whined.

"Okay, okay... Give me a minute to remember it first. I haven't thought about that one in a long time. Hmmm... Oh, now I remember. It had something to do with the tree cutters causing a stir amongst the whimsies," she said as she set a plate of bacon and eggs in front of each of them, then began the tale.

One summer's eve, long before you or I were born, the trine sprites sensed a foreboding in the glen where the whimsy trees they so lovingly cared for lived. When they went down to investigate, they found that many of their precious charges had been chopped down and carted away.

This was high summer, meaning that the whimsy trees were wide awake and growing strong, and had not been asked permission before their cuttings, as without going through the granting of permissions ceremony on the winter solstice, no awakened whimsy tree would give his or her permission to be reused for another purpose.

The remaining whimsies in the glen were outraged! In their shock and confusion, they needed someone to blame, and they were blaming humans, as it was by human hands their fellow trees had been cut down.

The trine sprites knew that not all humans were bad or evil people, but at the time there was no convincing the whimsies of this fact. They wanted the humans to pay, and were planning their revenge when the trine sprites came upon them. Some of the whimsies had already pulled up their roots and were teaching themselves how to move about.

The roots of the largest and oldest whimsies were too deeply entrenched in the soil and too intertwined with their soulmates, but the younger whimsies—those who had not yet found a forever partner—could, and were, uprooting themselves. They would be the warriors. They would save their remaining brother and sister trees, and remember, they could communicate with each other; they were planning and organizing an army to go down to the town far below and destroy the humans living there.

The trine sprites were understandably alarmed, and tried to calm the fears of their beloved whimsies. They said, "Let us handle this. We know humans, and we can safely find out who did this and why. You do not need to upset yourselves so."

But it was a hot and dry midsummer eve, and the whimsies were wide awake and so powerful during this time of year, and the trine sprites had never known them to be fighters before. So, try as they might, the trine sprites did not know how to calm the whimsies' fears, nor soothe their wrath.

The trine sprite Princess Toral called her two swiftest attendants to her, Zinnia and Pearl, and bid them seek out the pointer pair named Hither and Yon, for she needed more information to find the evil tree cutters and save the whimsies from their blighted self-destruction.

So, Zinnia and Pearl flew through the rocky terrain, staying well away from the caves and the claws of the wing snatchers and other mountain creatures. They flew up to the top of Pointers' Peak and there summoned Hither and Yon to come before them.

Zinnia and Pearl fluttered, unhappily exposed to the elements on the mountaintop as they awaited Hither and Yon. When the pointers finally appeared, it was as if they had materialized from the rock the sprites waited upon. Then they asked the trine sprites why they had been summoned on such a beautiful, warm summer's night.

Zinnia and Pearl explained what was happening to the whimsies and asked Hither and Yon to show them what led up to this and what would happen next. They said they needed to know for their princess in order to identify who hurt their whimsies and to return peace and harmony to their home.

Hither said, "I see men with axes, ropes, and wagons. I see a lord anxious for a new home, a powerful home that only he can control."

"Does this man have a name?" inquired Pearl.

"Yes!" answered Hither. "His name is Lord MacKenzie."

This shocked the trine sprites, as all knew Lord MacKenzie to be a kind and gentle man. Never had he taken a tree without going through the winter solstice granting of permissions ceremony. "There must be some mistake," said Pearl. "The MacKenzies of Loch MacKenzie are honorable and respectable people. Never have they taken a tree from our sacred wood without receiving permission to do so first."

"Did I say it was Lord Robert MacKenzie from Loch MacKenzie?" asked Hither.

"Well, no, you didn't," conceded Pearl. "But what other Lord MacKenzie is there?"

"There is another," stated Hither, "and it is he whom you must seek!"

"And where does this other live?" beseeched Pearl.

"He has fled across the sea and far away with the whimsies chopped down by the tree cutters," replied Hither. "Only the royal dolphins can show you the way."

"We don't have time for that now," Zinnia replied with concern.

Then they asked Yon what would happen next. Yon told them that depended on what occurred next, so Pearl asked, "If we do nothing and the whimsies go down to the village and attack the people, what will happen then?"

"The whimsies will attack the tree cutters and their families, of course!" replied Yon. "Then the whimsies may seek out Lord Robert MacKenzie and his family, and they might be killed as well because the whimsies only know that a MacKenzie did this to them."

Hither added, "This has never happened before. Now take our message back to Princess Toral, and swiftly. We will summon other pointer pairs to the peak and do what we can to help from here."

So quickly did the trine sprites fly down from Pointers' Peak and back to their princess with this news.

Robyn stopped at this point and shook her head. "Not one of you has touched your food—even you, Carson. Now eat! No more stories for now, as my to-do list is huge this morning."

Marlee said, "But Mom, what happens next?"

"Eat!" was all she said. "We'll continue this story another time."

Once she'd left, they toyed with their food—except for Carson, who ate all of his and part of Marlee's. Not wanting to stay in the house, and having a few hours to pass, they decided to do as their dad suggested and throw Carson's football around in the park.

A Promise Given

On the way to the park, Evan said to Marlee, "You know what happens next in the story, don't you?"

"More or less," replied Marlee. "But I never listened to it before, and I wanted to hear it again in case there was something we overlooked that could help us answer our questions."

"The whimsies couldn't have killed the good MacKenzies if they had remained inside Waterglenn, as the house would have protected them," Carson said. "But the queen wasn't there when she sent Maggie the message to leave immediately. I think they all panicked, cause no one had ever seen the whimsies act like this before. Maybe if we hear the tale of the tree cutters again. That's where we might get more information about Lord Ailbert and our great-aunt Maggie."

"Oh, but I've never heard that one," said Marlee quietly. "Mom always said it was too spooky for me 'cause of my nightmares."

"We need to ask May to tell us some of these stories. She'll have more information than Mom," he replied.

"Exactly what I was thinking," said Evan. "But she's out of town. I wonder where she went. Do you think it has anything to do with these pointers showing up?"

"Maybe," said Carson, trying to hide his own worry. *Would the mean house try to harm them again, and how could they protect themselves if it did?*

When they got to the park, Evan threw the football for Carson to catch, then practiced his own throws back for a while. Marlee was bored and wandered down the path toward the little cove and picnic table where they had sat with May.

She stopped to smell the white gardenias, and in so doing, thought she could hear part of a conversation. Unsure, she looked around to find its source. To her surprise, she saw two hummerlings drinking from some wild gardenia flowers in the next bush.

She said, "Oh! I'm sorry. I truly did not mean to eavesdrop."

As one of the birds sped away, the other turned and looked at Marlee as it rapidly fluttered its wings to hover in place for a few seconds. Then into Marlee's mind came the strangest command: "Three have been chosen. The queen of the sea comes. Wait here." Then the second hummerling quickly flew away out over the estuary.

The queen of the sea, thought Marlee. Who could this be, and chosen for what? She asked herself as she walked over to the old wooden picnic table and sat down facing the water.

Just as Marlee was about to give up and rejoin her brothers, they came looking for her. She told them what the hummerling had said to her, and so they decided to wait there together.

Each was into their own thoughts and questions when, once more, a deep amethyst head appeared from the water close to shore. This time they walked to the water's edge but did not go in. They could tell this was not King Koru, as this dolphin had brilliant blue-and-gold markings on its neck, so they waited and watched it swim around, then slowly raise its head once more above the waterline.

"Why do you not swim with me like you did my life partner, King Koru?" asked the royal dolphin into their minds.

"We were a bit confused by the hummerling's message," said Marlee. "Did she say we three have been chosen for something?"

"Ah," said the royal dolphin. "Let's begin with introductions, then. I am Queen Annika, life partner of King Koru. Together we have been tasked with maintaining the peace in this world's oceans."

"And I am Carson," said Carson, slowly taking a step closer to the river's edge.

"And I'm Evan," said Evan as he took one long jump in front of Carson.

"And you are Marlee, smallest of three with the biggest heart of all," said the queen to Marlee.

Marlee blushed, then asked again for what they had been chosen, and the queen of the sea explained.

"Many years ago, an evil was done in the forest of the whimsy trees. The person who committed this evil act is long dead, but the evil remains and has come down through the bloodline. There has been murder, thievery, and trickery committed by the heirs of Lord Sebastian MacKenzie, enough to match his own evil deeds when he knowingly, and in haste, tasked the tree cutters with murdering the strong young whimsies in high summer and without permission.

The seers of the old country are gathering here in the new to find a way to end this evil and still save the house built with the damaged whimsies. I believe you are now living in this house. Is this true?" the queen asked for confirmation.

"Yes it is," said Carson before the other two could respond. "And it tried to kill Marlee last night."

Startled, the queen looked at Marlee, who just nodded her head.

Then Marlee asked, "Are the seers of the old country the same as the pointer pairs?"

"Yes, I suppose that is their more modern name, though from our perspective they are more like troublemakers, as they tend to speak in riddles much of the time."

Then Evan asked impatiently, "But you didn't answer Marlee's question. For what have we three been chosen?"

"Ah," said the queen, understanding their confusion. "Why, to correct the wrong done to the whimsies and to heal the damaged house built with their wood."

"Ya right!" mumbled Carson sarcastically under his breath. Then he said out loud, "How can we do that when the house has already bitten Evan and now tried to suffocate Marlee? We don't even want to go back there today."

"Patience, young red-top," said the queen, using her nose to point to Carson's head of thick red hair. "All in good time."

"In whose good time?" asked Evan.

"Find the seers Hither and Yon. Once you find them, you will ask for their assistance in finding a way to repair the damage done to the house created with the murdered whimsy tree. However, you must pass and survive the caves of the wing snatchers in order to reach the peak from which you can call them."

"Why are there wing snatchers on the way to Pointers' Peak?" asked Marlee.

"Because the trine sprites go to the peak whenever they need the assistance of the seers. The wing snatchers know this, so they make their homes in the caves below."

"Will the wing snatchers attack us?" asked Marlee with growing concern.

Queen Annika nickered in her dolphin voice, then said to their minds once more, "That's a possibility if they are hungry. Use caution. Perhaps May can help you."

"But May is not here right now, and we don't know where she's gone," said Evan.

"Then wait until she returns, for it is also May who can tell you how to find the peak of the seers."

Then Evan's eyes lit up as he remembered what his mother had said about Princess Toral being in trine with a royal dolphin. So he asked the queen, "If the royal dolphins rule the sea, why do they care what happens on land?"

"I am in harmony trine with one who cares greatly," replied the queen. "Now I need your word that you will go to the peak and obtain this information. The seers' prophecy specifically states that three children of Dinsmore blood will avenge the wrong done to the whimsies."

"But we are MacKenzies, not Dinsmores," exclaimed Marlee. "Unless our great-aunt Maggie is the same as Ford's missing Maggie," she added, hopeful of solving one more riddle.

In response, Queen Annika told them that Maggie was the continuum, then once more requested their promise to do as she bid.

All three MacKenzies vowed to find Hither and Yon as soon as they could figure out how to do so, and with their promise, Queen Annika nodded regally to each in turn, then submerged and swam back out to the open sea.

Δ Δ Δ

Walking quickly, Carson, Evan, and Marlee returned to Ford, only to learn that no plan for dealing with Lord Ailbert had yet to be devised between Ford and the other houses on Dolphin Court.

As they were not due home for dinner for a while yet, they told Ford about the promise they'd made to Queen Annika, and asked him if he knew what the dolphin queen meant when she said that Maggie was the continuum.

Thoughtful, Ford replied slowly, "Since her arrival a long time ago, Maggie has always been here—or was, until she and the rest of my family disappeared."

"But is she our great-aunt Maggie or not?" asked Carson, needing a direct answer. "I mean, if it was her brother Captain Dinsmore who founded Waters End and built you, Ford, then that's how we could have Dinsmore blood, but this is also impossible. How can a human live this long?"

"When you go to the peak, ask the pointers," answered Ford. "They will know."

Wing Snatcher-Thingies

That evening when Robyn was saying goodnight to her children, Carson said, "Tonight is my turn for a story, and I want to hear about the wing snatchers again."

Robyn looked at Marlee rather surprised, as she usually objected to hearing this tale, but for some reason she did not object tonight. A bit confused, their mother said, "Well, I suppose so. If you're sure, I'll tell that one but leave the scary parts out."

"Oh no!" cried Marlee. "I want to hear the whole story from beginning to end."

"Well, if you say so, my poppet. You sure have grown up since we came to Waters End." And so she began telling the tale of the wing snatchers.

When the sprites sought a pointer pair, they needed to fly up to Pointers' Peak, and this was not pleasant as the peak was high above the grotto where the trine sprites lived, and there was no water anywhere around it. Since the trine sprites drew their strength from water, they could die if they went too far astray and for too long a time without it. Plus, there were no trees on this mountain peak, so the sprites had no protection from the fierce mountain winds, or the unfriendly creatures known to inhabit the caves nearby.

Some of these creatures had large fangs and treacherous claws. A little trine sprite was like a small dessert to them. When they flew close to the ground, as they were wont to do when the winds were blowing, they could be snatched up quickly by a many-pronged claw or whipped unconscious by a barbed tail. Either way, they were done for if that happened.

One particularly vicious creature was called a wing snatcher. Wing snatchers were not often sociable. Unless they wanted a mate, which was seldom, they lived alone in their own caves. They were much larger than the sprites, averaging six or seven feet tall. Also, they had only one pair of dull-gray wings that were too small for their size, meaning they could not fly far—maybe only as far as the house next door.

When a wing snatcher was near his cave door he could always tell if a trine sprite was close by, as his own wings would begin to tingle and hum a minute or so before the trine sprite appeared. Because of this, some said that wing snatchers were related to the trine sprites from many generations back. Your great-aunt Maggie said she thought they were jealous of the sprites' beauty and abilities, and captured the trine sprites because of this.

Robyn stopped at this point. "Marlee, are you sure you want me to cover the scary parts?"

"Yes, Mama," Marlee replied. Evan and Carson were on either side of her and took her hands for strength as their mother continued the tale.

Well, the story says that the wing snatchers would (when they could, that is) knock a poor, unsuspecting trine sprite unconscious as she or he flew by one of their caves, then tie the sprite's feet to a rope attached to a tall stake in the ground. The wing snatcher would then amuse itself watching the helpless trine sprite fly round and round in a circle till, so exhausted, the sprite collapsed on the ground. Sometimes it would throw food at the poor sprite, who desperately tried to catch it and could not because the wing snatcher threw it just out of reach.

Just before the trine sprite died, the wing snatcher would cut off the sprite's wings and mount them on a wall in his cave as a sort of prize, giving the wing snatcher bragging rights amongst his kind. Because the wings were cut before the sprite died, they lived on without their sprite, maintaining their color and fluttering occasionally, still seeking the sprite from whence they came.

It was tragic when a trine sprite died in this manner. Not only did the immediate family and other sprites mourn the loss, but the whimsy trees tended by that sprite grieved the loss as well. The trees sometimes refused to share water from the enchanted pool or communicate with the other trees for a long, long time; some even died themselves in the process.

Because of the inherent danger, trine sprites normally travelled in pairs when they went to call the pointers or when they needed to travel over the terrain inhabited by the wing snatchers. Great-aunt Maggie never mentioned a wing snatcher being able to subdue two sprites at once, possibly because of the sprites' own charms. They may be small, but they are strong in their own way.

As Robyn finished the tale, she searched her daughter's face for signs of fear or sadness. Finding none, she was heartened and confused at the same time.

Carson noted this, saying, "She's okay, Mom. Really. We just needed to know what the wing snatchers were capable of. I mean, with so many of great-aunt Maggie's tales coming true and all…" Then Carson remembered

Marlee was with them and decided not to say anything more. He knew all three of them were about to face this danger. Somehow, they were going to find the peak and carry out their promise to the royal dolphin Queen Annika.

MIFFED WITH MARLEE

The second night in the mean house was uneventful. Marlee had no nightmares, though Carson and Evan slept barely a wink with worry that the house might again try to hurt her in some way.

Waiting for May's return was becoming rather dull, so again they went by Ford's to look for anything unusual about him that he may have missed since losing his family. Finding nothing, they went to the park so that Carson could practice his throws and catches.

On the way home for lunch, Marlee wasn't excited about the prospect of going back to the mean house so soon. Instead, she told her brothers she was stopping at the local drugstore for some gum and would catch up to them in a bit.

She bought a pack of Juicy Fruit for herself and then some fruit sours for Evan and Carson, as she knew they liked them. Then she slowly began the walk back to their new home. She was in no hurry to return to the mean house, and there was no way she would call the house Lord Ailbert. *No,* she was thinking as she began to walk slower and slower, almost dragging her feet, not paying attention to anything other than her wish to be going to any home but this one.

"Why do you wish for this?" asked a quiet voice next to her.

Startled, Marlee looked up to see a pointer walking alongside her. "Oh!" she said in surprise. "I didn't hear you approach. Can you really read my mind?" she asked, curious and happy to finally meet one.

"Sometimes," replied the pointer. "You're one of the new MacKenzie children who have recently moved into Lord Ailbert, aren't you?" he asked kindly.

"Well if you can really read my mind, then you ought to already know that," chastised Marlee in her most adult voice.

"Sorry," responded the pointer. "I can see you don't want to be bothered, so I'll be on my way."

"No, don't go!" pleaded Marlee. "I didn't mean to be rude, and we—that is, my brothers and I," she said more softly, "we've been trying to find and meet you."

"Why do you want to meet us?" inquired the pointer.

Her voice grew in agitation as she thought of all the mysteries they'd encountered. "To help us answer some of our questions about this town, its houses, and our great-great-aunt Maggie and her missing family. And now Queen Annika has made us promise to find Pointers' Peak and ask a question of Hither and Yon, and we don't even know where the peak is yet, as May's out of town, and Queen Annika said we need May's help to get started, and..."

"Hush now, little Marlee MacKenzie," said the pointer, gently stopping her from her tirade. "All in good time," he finished soothingly.

At that moment, another pointer appeared on Marlee's other side. "Maybe we can help you, young Marlee. But in order to do so, you must tell us our together name and individual names. These are the rules, and the Beginner help us if we are ever caught not abiding by them," he chuckled.

Marlee thought for a moment. Because her mother had mentioned the pointer pair known as Waste-Not and Want-Not, and these two seemed so caring of her welfare, she wondered if they could be them, but she didn't know what their together name could be. In her mind she kept asking herself: if there is no waste and there is no want, then what is there?

The second pointer to join them was getting a little impatient with her by this time, so he asked his own question. "Miss Marlee, if I can stand on one leg and not wobble, what am I doing well?"

As Marlee continued to stare at him blankly, he tried to help her a bit more by saying, "If I can stand well on one leg, wouldn't I have a good sense of something?"

"Oh!" exclaimed Marlee. "That would never have occurred to me. Your together name is Balance, then. Is that correct?"

"Phew!" said the second. "This is getting harder and harder these days," he sighed as he shook his head.

"True," said the first pointer with a smirk. He turned to Marlee and asked her if she could tell them their individual names.

Remembering the story her mother told about Carson wanting but not needing a new bicycle, she asked, "If I could go to the moon and paint it any color I wanted to, what color would I choose?"

Waste-Not and Want-Not conferred for a moment, then the first pointer said, "Painting the moon is ridiculous. There is not enough paint on this planet with which to do so."

Then the second pointer asked his own question. "Why would you want to go to the moon in the first place, much less paint it?"

Marlee giggled at their responses and properly identified each, because Waste-Not was more concerned about the waste in time and effort to go to and paint the moon, and Want-Not saw no reason to go to the moon at all, much less to paint it.

After Marlee told them their individual names, Waste-Not still wanted to know what color Marlee would have chosen to paint the moon. She simply answered, "Pink. It's my favorite color."

"Pink," said Waste-Not. "Of course, you are a young girl. I should have thought of that," he said, smiling kindly. "Now that you have properly identified us, we can answer your questions. So ask away, little Marlee who loves all things pink."

"Let me ask her what she wants before we attempt to answer her questions," interjected Want-Not.

As Waste-Not agreed, Marlee said, "I want to live in a peaceful home—one that does not try to kill me. And I want my brothers and my mother and father to be happy and to laugh and play with me again like they did before we moved here," she finished rather forlornly.

"Then see it as already done, young Marlee," said Want-Not slowly and hypnotically. "Look inside yourself. Feel how you would feel if you had everything you ever wanted that mattered. Your cares are gone. What you want you already have deep inside you. Let it out, little one. Let it out... Feel it... See it," he finished with a hiss.

Marlee's eyes began to close slightly, and she sighed a great sigh as if a huge weight had been lifted from her shoulders. Yes, she could see it, she thought, and she could feel it, too. It was wonderful, and she felt so peaceful as somehow she continued to walk home, for the next thing she knew Evan and Carson were greeting her on Lord Ailbert's small front porch.

"Hey you!" said Carson rather loudly. "We were afraid you'd gotten lost and were coming to look for you."

"Uh-oh," exclaimed Evan, looking at Marlee's expression with worry. "Carson, look at her eyes. She's not all the way here. They look kinda foggy or something. Go get Mom, and quick, okay?"

When their mother joined them on the front porch, Marlee was becoming more herself again and didn't understand what all the fuss was about, so she told them about meeting Waste-Not and Want-Not and guessing their together and individual names correctly.

In their excitement over Marlee meeting and speaking to a pointer pair, they forgot all about her dreamy state of a few moments before; that is, they forgot all about it until later that evening, when Carson and Evan wanted to learn more about them and Marlee was so vague in her responses it was as if she no longer cared.

It started when Carson pulled out their questions list from his back pocket. "We need to add the pointer pair Waste-Not and Want-Not to the list of characters we've now met in this new town. Marlee, what did they look like? Did they look the same as the others we've seen?"

Marlee looked at Carson a bit confused, then sighed softly. "Yes, they looked just like the other pointy-headed people we've seen, Carson."

"Well," said Evan, "were they nice and friendly? Did you get to ask any of the questions we've got?"

"Oh, I guess I forgot all about the questions list," Marlee said rather distantly.

"What do you mean, you forgot about our list?" said Carson, his voice rising. "There is so much we need to know in order to solve all these riddles around us," he finished as his frustration with her lack of enthusiasm mounted.

"I mean, don't you remember the other night when Lord Ailbert tried to kill you? Doesn't that mean anything to you?"

"Oh, Carson," Marlee replied. "That was probably just one of my Marlee-mares. I don't want to believe that a house tried to kill me. I mean, would you want to believe that if you had a choice?"

Both Carson and Evan were stunned; they felt Marlee was no longer interested in their quest or the promise they'd made to Queen Annika. In fact, Marlee didn't appear to care about much of anything at all. *Oh, if only May were here,* the two brothers thought. *She'd know what's going on and how to fix it.*

May Returns

The next day, Carson and Evan left Lord Ailbert early for May's Best, hoping she had returned. When they inquired, they were told she was expected back any time. Not knowing what else to do while they waited, and definitely not wanting to return home and confront Marlee again, they headed out to the cove at the end of the city park.

As they sat at the old wooden picnic table on the sand, a hummerling approached them. The boys ignored it as they continued looking out over the water. Perplexed, the hummerling flew between them and whirred so loudly that they finally had to turn their heads and look at it.

Introducing himself, the hummerling said, "My name is Thor, and May asked me to find you. What now, children of the chosen?"

Being polite, Evan said, "Nice to meet you, Thor." Then his shoulders drooped, and once again he looked out to the river and beyond.

Thor could tell something wasn't right with the boys, as he had only experienced their laughter before. "Wait here!" he suddenly commanded. "May is coming," he said as he quickly departed, anxious to find her current whereabouts.

Evan and Carson barely acknowledged Thor's departure as they slightly lifted their heads up, then slowly moved them down again before returning to gaze at the calmly flowing water once more.

Concerned that three had become two, and that the two were not happy at all, Thor darted off to find May. He finally found her coming down the hill from the old Indian burial grounds.

Thor fluttered in May's face, conveying the news that three had become two, and appeared quite despondent in the process. In return, May acknowledged Thor's message by picking up her pace as she hurried down to the bottom of the hill where her car was parked. As she stepped inside her car, she bade Thor to find Marlee and ask her to join them at the cove.

May had many things on her mind, one of which was the news that Edward Edwards had found the location of the old silver mine, and that he had been going there looking for silver. Yon had also told her that Edward had befriended Beezos, a particularly evil wing snatcher.

Though hurrying as much as was safe, it still took May some time to reach her restaurant, park, then speak to her staff to ensure all their needs were met before she could walk down to the cove to see how Carson and Evan were doing.

May was disturbed that the three MacKenzie children were not together, and even more so that Evan and Carson appeared sad and lost. Hither and Yon had given her both good and bad news up on the peak, and if she hadn't stopped to discuss a few issues with Princess Toral and the younger whimsies, she would have returned the night before as originally planned.

Just as May approached the city park, Thor flew up to her once again, saying that the young Marlee would not speak with him. May feared this, as it meant that Hither was correct in his vision of Marlee meeting the pointer pair Waste-Not and Want-Not.

May asked Thor to keep an eye on Marlee while she went to get Carson and Evan. She asked Thor to entice Marlee to the mound at the back of Lord Ailbert and to keep her there until May and the boys could join them.

As May walked quickly down to the cove, she slowed her steps rounding the bend to observe the brothers firsthand without them seeing her. She found them just the way Thor had described them...shoulders hunched as they gazed half-seeing out over the estuary.

Turning the bend with purpose in her stride once more, she called out, "Carson, Evan! To me, now! We've got to rush. I've just come down from the new Pointers' Peak and we haven't a moment to lose. Follow me quickly!" she ended as she made an about-facc and staned back up the path out of the park.

Carson and Evan were elated to see her again, and followed her gladly. When they got to May's car, she took off almost before Carson had shut his door and hurried back to Dolphin Court. As May pulled up, the boys were startled, as they did not expect May to takc them back to Lord Ailbert.

May turned to them. "Marlee will join us in the cavern."

"What cavern?" exclaimed Evan.

"Hush," returned May. "No questions yet. Follow me through the back gate."

As they approached the mound at the back of Lord Ailbert's rear yard, they saw Marlee laughing and humming along to a song Thor was singing to her.

"Have you ever seen such an enchanting bird?" asked Marlee while she gracefully danced to a tune the hummerling was singing.

"Thank you, Thor. It's my turn to owe you a favor now," May said as she smoothed away dirt from the backside of the mound, revealing an old, round metal door upon which she knocked three times to open.

"Carson," she said, "you lead the way. Evan will follow you, then Marlee. I will bring up the rear. The torches lit automatically when I knocked on the door along with the fireplace down below, but it is still dim and a bit chilly down there compared to up here, so let your eyes adjust for a moment as you begin your descent."

Carson and Evan were thrilled to enter this secret place, but Marlee hung back, confused and alarmed. "Why am I going into this hole?"

she asked, sticking out her lower lip to show her displeasure.

"It's a surprise, little one," said May. "And it will make you even happier than Thor's singing."

Marlee heard Carson's thrill of delight as he exclaimed how beautiful it was inside. "Oh!" exclaimed Marlee. "Then I will be glad to follow my brothers," she said as she began the climb down the smooth, torch-lit stairs.

Lord Sebastian's Cavern

Once they were all assembled at the long table where just a few days earlier several pointer pairs had held their own secret meeting, Carson and Evan immediately started flinging questions at May.

Holding up her hands, May said, "Cease! I cannot even hear myself think when you talk so. Let me explain where you are and what I've learned. Then you can ask all the questions you want."

May told them the history of the cavern. "The original Lord Sebastian MacKenzie had this cavern built for his own use, for no sooner had he created his powerful new home than he realized it had a few drawbacks, such as personal privacy. So he added the cavern beneath the rear yard to provide some sanctuary for himself and his closest chums, and even his wife when they needed to discuss matters best left unheard by Lord Ailbert and their children.

"To keep it private, the cavern runs the entire length of Lord Ailbert's rear yard but does not touch Lord Ailbert's walls nor join his own basement, meaning that it truly is safe down here, as Lord Ailbert cannot hear anything we say or see anything we do."

May took a deep breath and continued talking. "Now, I have just returned from the new Pointers' Peak. Evan, you were correct that there is one here, and I was correct in that it is indeed above the old Indian burial grounds up on the bluff outside town."

May told the children that she had called both Hither and Yon to her up on the peak and asked them a series of questions. In exchange, they had told her what may happen next and what could then occur.

Evan's hand shot up as he realized why the pointers met here now, and before he could say a word, May said, "Yes, Evan. They sometimes meet here too, especially Hither and Yon. Which brings me to my next question. I hear that you met the royal dolphin

Queen Annika while I was up the hill and that she has promised you to a quest. Is this so?"

"Yes," said Carson and Evan, glad that May was finally going to address one of their concerns.

"The hummerling Thor has told me that she has called you 'the chosen' from Yon's prophecy."

"Right again," acknowledged Carson as he recited what Queen Annika bid them to do. "'Find the seers Hither and Yon. Once you find them, you will ask for their assistance in finding a way to repair the damage done to the house created with the murdered Whimsy trees.'"

"But she also said three children from Captain Jon Dinsmore's family were the chosen," wailed Evan, "and we aren't Dinsmores—we're MacKenzies."

"Hmmm…and that is a mystery we still need to solve. Regardless, after speaking with Hither and Yon, I believe you are the chosen as well," May ended.

"But chosen for what?" Carson lamented. "We're just kids. And now with Marlee going weird, Evan and I don't know what to do."

"Let's start at the beginning then, Carson. Where is your questions list?" May asked gently.

Carson once more pulled the list from his back pocket and slowly read each question aloud. While he was doing so, Evan was ticking them off one by one with his fingers to make sure none were missed, and Marlee was watching the candles flicker in their crystal sconces while humming to herself as if she hadn't a care in the world.

May thought for a moment, then told the children what she knew so far: that the living houses on Dolphin Court were built from the whimsy trees just like in the faery tale. She also told them she knew how they could get to the new Pointers' Peak.

Finally, she told them that she now believed that both their Maggies had to be the same person, though she did not as yet know how this could be, but if true, then of course they would be not just MacKenzies, but Dinsmores, too.

As Carson was writing down the answers, Evan asked May, "If you are part trine sprite, are you in trine with Thor? Is that why he came to find us?"

As May nodded yes, Evan quickly asked, "Then who is your third partner in trine?"

May looked at Marlee, who still seemed to care so little for what was going on around her. Then she asked, "Marlee, who do you think my third in trine is?"

Thinking this but another game, Marlee giggled, and in her current Want-Not-induced state of mind, said in a sly tone, "Well, you run a restaurant with the freshest fruits and vegetables I've ever tasted, and Ford's garden is the most abundant and well cared for I have ever seen. Therefore, I think you're in trine with Ford!" she finished, proud of herself and her reasoning.

May gave Marlee a studious look, then replied merrily, "Close! Close, my dear."

"If not Ford, then someone else who lives in Ford's home!" Marlee said, finally getting excited.

Evan's eyes widened as the answer came to him, and he shot up his hand as if in the schoolroom, begging May to let him speak.

May's eyes twinkled. "Do you know, Evan?"

"It's the climbing tree, isn't it?" he asked as he turned to Marlee and reminded her of how she was too short to reach the bottom branch, but then somehow she could.

Marlee's eyes opened wide, and she smiled prettily as she remembered the fun they had had climbing that tree in Ford's backyard.

"What's its name?" asked Carson.

"She is the Princess Marbella," replied May. "The first whimsy tree planted in the new world, and the third member of my harmony trine."

"So that's what a whimsy tree looks like," said Carson in awe.

"But what is your trine name, then?" asked Evan.

May waved her right arm gently toward the fireplace and opened her palm upward. As she did so, the fire appeared to leap higher, jewel-toned colors springing forth and flitting around the room, shining brightly and moving softly as if being blown by a quiet summer breeze.

Again May turned her palm upward, and this time a blue-green orb floated over to their table. Slowly the glowing orb hovered before each child, then gently touched their foreheads, acknowledging their presence.

Returning to May, the orb spoke in a strong and clear voice. "I am Turquoise, bearer of truth, seeker of knowledge and understanding. May and her trine only speak the truth, so hear her now," it ended in a whisper, then faded back into the once more quietly-burning fire along with the other orbs.

At that moment, Marlee began to whimper and to cry softly. She felt her head where the orb had touched it and complained of a burning feeling.

In concern, Evan and Carson rushed to her side of the table and put their arms around her as they looked up at May for guidance.

"She's alright now," May informed them. "My trine's strength has broken Want-Not's spell, and though she is sad because she can no longer escape into her daydreams, she is back with us once more."

Carson lovingly held Marlee as she wept softly while Evan told her she would always be the best sister in the world.

"Now!" May said, her energy and spirit returning. "We need to make plans for getting you three up to the peak and calling Hither and Yon."

"But aren't you coming with us?" Carson asked.

"No," replied May. "The prophecy specially states three children of Captain Jon Dinsmore's bloodline and none other. I will see you when you return."

"But we can't be... Oh, forget it," Carson grumbled again at the mysteries still unsolved.

As the four of them discussed the best path and plans for getting to the peak, the day turned into early evening, and May told them it was time to leave, for the pointer pairs might be meeting in the cavern tonight, and they needed to leave before then.

PART 3 — FINDING

Finders keepers...losers weepers, and so the rhyme goes. And in the finding, are we satisfied? Does finding give us answers, or create more questions? Only time will tell.

WING SNATCHER BAIT

Outside of town, in a small, old house mostly hidden by overgrown bushes and scraggly trees, Edward Edwards pondered his next steps. He wanted time to finish reading the family journals he had found the day he lost his home. Some of the entries provided significant clues as to his true heritage.

Once he understood that he too was a MacKenzie by blood, he began to like the idea that he was descended from a lord. He imagined what he would do if he actually was one—but he needed money and lots of it, for a royal title with no means of support meant nothing.

While continuing to read his family's journals, he looked more closely at the land grant for a silver mine and the deed to the land. After verifying with the county that the land still belonged to his family, he purchased mining equipment and proceeded to locate both the proposed and revised entrances to the mine.

The real clue as to the value of the silver mine came to him through another entry in his ancestor Elizabeth's journal.

My poor father and mother have been gone several years now and I still haven't found a way to get the silver mine approved by the town council. Though I love my Mr. Edwards, he refuses to do anything that is not completely legal. He does not understand the value of the silver mine and how much wealthier we could be were we to make a business of it.

My father knew how to make things happen, and when he was younger he had ultimate control over old Bertie here. Though a child at the time, I overheard him command the house to intimidate or eliminate all those who dared to interfere with his plans to accumulate wealth and power. When Lord MacKenzie needed a land grant to develop a silver mine near the old Indian burial grounds, Mr. Miller, a local engineer and archeologist, opposed him. One day my father asked Mr. Miller to call so they could discuss their differences of opinion as to the construction of the mine and the preservation of the sacred Indian burial grounds.

Though Mr. Miller agreed to return to the hill and verify the appropriateness of Lord Sebastian's new mine entrance, he was still opposed to the building of it under the Indians' sacred hill.

Mr. Miller disappeared that very day. Lord Sebastian told the town constable that yes, he and Mr. Miller had met to discuss their opposing views on the mine issue. He showed the constable a copy of a map he had given Mr. Miller depicting an alternate entrance to the mine that would not impact the sacred burial grounds on the hill outside of town.

Lord MacKenzie said the last he had seen of Mr. Miller was his departure to visit the hill and study the new location of the silver mine. As no one in town could say differently, and only the body of Mr. Miller's horse was ever found on the rocks by the water below, it was surmised that Mr. Miller and his horse must have fallen off the cliff and his body swept out to sea by the fast-moving current in the middle of the estuary.

Ha! I knew that was a lie. My father almost always got his way—except, of course, when he got in my way.

Yes, Edward thought to himself, *my long-lost MacKenzie relative was a mover and a shaker, but times have changed.* He wasn't going to appeal for a license to run the mine. Not yet, anyway. He would start mining it himself and see where that led him first.

Within a few days, he found a hidden cave entrance that led to a tunnel on one side of the proposed mine site. After careful investigation, he chose this spot to set up his personal mining operation. From the first day he found silver, and plenty of it. While reading books and comparing pictures of silver veins, he had amassed over fifty pounds of the precious ore with little effort at all.

Had it not been for his right hand, infected by the spider that had bitten him before he lost his home, he would have had double this amount by now. Cursing, he kept up his pace, working as hard as he could and ignoring his hand till it went numb and would no longer do his bidding.

Beezos

One day while Edward was talking to himself in the silver mine, he heard a deep, calm voice ask, "Why digging shiny earth?"

Moving slowly with his pickaxe lethally positioned in his right hand, Edward turned a complete circle, looking for the body attached to the voice.

"Up here, silly human," came the voice once more, and this time Edward looked up. As the miner's lamp on his helmet shone upward, he froze. About ten feet above him, at the entrance to a tunnel Edward had not noticed before, sat a hideous, grayish creature with a square face, heavy jowls, tiny eyes, and bushy, overgrown eyebrows. The creature appeared to be smiling down at him, but his canine-pointed teeth made the smile seem more like a leer.

Temporarily blinded by Edward's light, the creature shielded his eyes with a large, six-clawed hand. Edward seized the moment to make a dash for the cave entrance. Before he got far, the creature was upon him.

"Stop!" it yelled as it reached out and grabbed Edward by the back of his jacket and lifted him fully off his feet to swing in the air like a rag doll, knocking his helmet off in the process.

The creature laughed deeply, making a hoarse croaking sound as it grinned even wider at Edward.

Seeing no alternative, Edward finally found his voice and asked imperiously, "What are your intentions?"

Confused by Edward's formal tone and apparent lack of fear, the creature replied, "To talk with you, stupid human."

"Then put me down first, for I'm not about to talk when I'm being held dangling above the ground," replied Edward with his own elegant sneer neatly in place once more.

"Only if you don't try and run away again," jeered the creature in return.

Edward agreed, but objected to the dark tunnel. In return, the creature flew him to the upper tunnel entrance, then carried him through to a large cavern where a slow fire was burning. It dropped Edward with a thump on one side of the fire and lumbered over to the other, giving some distance between them.

Sitting down rather quickly, his legs buckling beneath him, Edward asked, "What are you?"

"My name is Beezos, and I think your name is Lord Edward MacKenzie, for I have been listening to you talk to yourself for a while now," replied Beezos, grinning devilishly again.

"But I mean, *what* are you?" asked Edward.

"Why, I guess your people call us wing snatchers," Beezos laughed as he pointed to the two pairs of trine sprite wings on the walls of his cavern, still fluttering and glowing dimly in their soft, translucent colors.

"Hmmm," muttered Edward. "Those don't look like your wings, as they are small and brightly colored. What creature did they come from?"

"Why, from the sprites, of course," answered Beezos. By the look on Edward's face, Beezos could tell he did not know what a sprite was, so he began telling him about how delectable they were to eat, yet so difficult to catch.

Getting bored with the description of the wing snatcher's favorite food, Edward looked away and surmised his situation. He did not know these upper caverns existed, and he could see even larger silver veins up here. In fact, the glow from the fire made them shine brightly as he counted at least ten wide veins a few inches in width running up and down the sides of the cavern.

"Well, now we've met and had a nice chat," said Edward. "If you don't mind, I have work to do in the cavern below and not much time to get it done."

Surprised, Beezos asked again why Edward was digging the shiny earth.

Annoyed, Edward replied that he owned this mine and could do with it as he pleased.

Laughing with his low, croaking voice once more, Beezos said, "No one owns the earth. This was my home long before you appeared. You are only alive right now due to my generosity," he finished with a wide, cruel smile that showed off his fierce, sharp fangs. As Edward began to rethink his next move, Beezos studied him, then offered a suggestion.

"I think you may be of use to me, so I will not eat you yet. And if you help me, then maybe I can help you get more of the shiny earth you want so much."

As Edward finally looked him in the eye, Beezos said, "I need another set of trine sprite wings to decorate my walls, and they've become difficult to catch lately."

Thinking that this may turn to his advantage after all, Edward asked slyly, "How can I help you?"

Beezos told Edward his plan to lure a sprite to his newest cave entrance, and together they devised a plot that even Edward thought was brilliant!

As Edward stood up to leave, he placed weight on his right hand, then yelped in pain.

This was the hand the spider had bitten the day before he lost his home, and it had never healed. The back of his hand was turning green with dark edges, and it was swollen half again as large as his left hand.

Beezos growled. "You can't help me if you don't fix that hand. It's already sending poison through the rest of you." Beezos quickly walked up to Edward, took his arm as if to study his hand, and before Edward could protest, sliced it off with a sharp blade.

Spellbound for just a moment, Edward felt the pain shooting up his arm as Beezos, holding his arm more tightly now, gathered hot ash from the fire with his bare hands and cauterized the stump that used to be Edward's right hand.

Terrified and in shock, Edward fainted dead away.

Beezos caught him before he fell and laid him on a straw mat next to the fire. Mumbling to himself as he fixed a proper poultice to stop Edward's bleeding, he realized he was hungry. Edward's hand caught his eye. He picked it up and turned it over, looking for the source of the infection.

Ha! he thought, finally appreciating the human's strength. Beezos saw the two tiny bite marks on Edward's hand, most likely delivered by one of the sprite's spider friends. Their venom was deadly to most animals; even wing snatchers had died when bitten by more than one at a time.

Bending down to a pot by the fire, Beezos brewed a concoction to numb Edward's pain and draw out the remaining venom from his body. As he did so, he imagined three sets of trine sprite wings for his cave wall. Once he had the next set of sprite wings, he would be the most powerful wing snatcher on the hill, and soon Edward Edwards would disappear and no longer disrupt his cave with his constant banging on the walls for the shiny earth he so coveted.

Obsessed with these thoughts, Beezos tended Edward until he was well enough to carry out their plan.

POINTERS' PEAK

As they left Lord Sebastian's cavern, May reminded the children to pack lightly for the next day's adventure explaining that she would bring whatever supplies they needed.

When they returned home, Carson, Evan, and Marlee hurried upstairs to wash up for dinner. Once the family was seated, Carson followed the plan they'd made by telling his parents that May had invited them all to her beachside cottage for a few days before school began.

Excited by the opportunity to relax at the beach, their mom thought this an excellent idea. But their dad reminded them that unpacking wasn't finished yet, and that they still had a lot to do before school started. Then unexpectedly, he waved his hand in a mock farewell, quickly deciding that yes, this would be good for them and for himself, as he would have time to get caught up on his work.

Δ Δ Δ

At dawn the next morning, Marlee knocked on Evan's door and entered to see her brothers staring out the window. Together they watched the pointers leave the mound quickly in pairs, dispersing in different directions as they left.

"May was right again," Carson said as he turned from the window and sat down on his bed. Though they all loved hiking, he knew it was his responsibility to get them safely to and from the peak. Being the eldest had never bothered him till now, with May's constant warnings about the best path to take to avoid not only the trine sprites and the wing snatchers, but now Edward Edwards and the silver mine as well.

Always the optimist, Evan spoke his thoughts aloud. "Hey! Why so doom and gloom? We're about to begin the best adventure of our lives! Can you even imagine meeting a trine sprite, wing snatchers, pointer pairs, and who knows what else in person? I am so stoked!"

As usual, Evan's excitement pierced Carson and Marlee's doubts and helped them feel stronger. Then Marlee made him feel even better when she said, "At least we have each other and we are three, so we're the MacKenzie Trine, powerful in our own right!"

Getting the last word in, Evan put on his best stage performer's voice. "What we have here are attention to detail (Carson), quickness and agility (me), and of course, common sense (Marlee-bo-barley)."

"I am not a grain. I'm a person," quipped Marlee as she smiled, delighted to be called her nickname from years ago.

Hearing their mother's voice down the hall, they quickly went to their rooms to finish getting ready. Ten minutes later, with their gear stored by the front door, they were in the kitchen watching their mom cook a hearty breakfast to keep them going throughout the day.

"Ah-ha, there you are," she said. "I spoke with May last night. So, we aren't going to the beach after all, right?"

"Shhh!" said Carson quietly as he slowly mouthed that Lord Ailbert could be listening to all that they said.

Unhappy with his reply, their mother puckered her lips, turned, and continued to serve breakfast.

Nelson came down the stairs just as May knocked on the front door. Eager for some time alone, he welcomed her with a broad smile and introduced himself efficiently.

Tilting her head a bit, May looked up to the father of this household appraising him. *His handshake was firm but not too tight, his eyes clear, and their was genuine warmth in his smile. All good signs that there was hope for him yet.*

Δ   Δ   Δ

Their goodbyes made, they drove off with May and parked in Ford's garage at the back of his property so that none would see May's car.

Waterford welcomed them inside and asked what their plans were and if he could help. May informed him that the children were going to Pointers' Peak to speak with Hither and Yon, and that she and Robyn were going to visit the abandoned silver mine and find out what Edward Edwards was up to.

Turning to inspect the children's backpacks, May checked each carefully, ensuring they had what they might need on this quest. Special equipment consisted of flashlights, wooden matches, thick cotton balls to start a fire if needed, and a simple first-aid kit in case of trouble. For some reason they had yet to discover, electronics didn't work well on the peak, so they decided to leave their cell phones and other gadgets at Ford's.

As they were about to leave, Waterford stopped them with a simple question. "What tools have you brought for protection?"

Robyn and May were surprised, as they had never considered this possibility, so Waterford invited them up to his third and highest floor, where the outline of a closet door faded into view on a wall covered with a pale powder-blue, silver, and white-striped wallpaper.

As the two sides of the door opened wide, they revealed shelves stacked high with toys and books, plus items not normally found in a child's closet.

Waterford said, "I made this closet for my missing children. It holds their favorite things, all waiting for their return. Perhaps there is something here you can use in case of trouble."

Carson's eye focused immediately upon the middle shelf, where he spied a dark green leather-handled dagger. Balancing the weight of the dagger in his right hand, it fit perfectly in his palm, so he gently slid the dagger from its case. Sunlight through the window touched the blade, revealing an inscription of some kind on one side, though not in a language he could read. The script was long and the words narrow—at least, he thought they were words, as there was some spacing between the groupings of symbols.

Reaching for the dagger, May studied the inscription. She informed them it was obviously in trine sprite, as she recognized some of the letters from their written language, but the only word she could decipher was 'defend.' Handing it back to Carson, she made a mental note to ask Princess Toral about this dagger when next they met.

Pleased, Waterford told them that the dagger belonged to Kyle, the eldest son of his missing family, and that he didn't think Kyle would mind Carson's borrowing it.

Excited, Carson promised Waterford he'd take good care of it, then showed the dagger to Evan and Marlee. *At least we have something to defend ourselves with now,* he thought as he again balanced the dagger in his hand before returning it to its protective sheath.

Waterford asked Evan to select something from the cupboard. Excited, Evan took his time, even pulling out a footstool so he could peer into the top shelf more easily. When his left hand finally fell upon an opaque crystal, he knew he had found his gift. Almost immediately the crystal grew warm to his touch, then began to burn his palm from the inside, forcing him to let it go.

May snatched the glowing crystal from the carpet, lest it start a fire, and placed it in the thick purple suede pouch on the shelf next to it. The pouch had a soft and sturdy leather thong attached to it, so she dropped it over Evan's head, saying, "You have chosen well, young Evan. This is a healing crystal. Where Carson's blade may defend you, you will be able to heal by placing the crystal on an injury. Of course, there are some trine sprite words that are usually spoken when doing this; alas, I do not know them. Hopefully using the crystal alone may be good enough in a pinch."

Finally it was Marlee's turn to choose. Unbeknownst to the others, she had spied her gift the moment the cupboard doors opened, and had patiently waited her turn, knowing her brothers would never have selected this object. She quickly reached in for the small silver bell, the type normally hung on Christmas trees. Marlee rang the bell, bringing forth a sound so melodious and pure that it echoed through all of Ford's rooms, and seemed to increase in volume even after Marlee ceased ringing it.

May was pleased, and told Marlee to use the bell if they got lost or needed assistance. She told them that though she was only part trine sprite, even she could hear this bell when rung from a great distance and would do her best to heed its call.

Stuffing the bell firmly into the little top change pocket of her jeans, Marlee hoped she'd never need to ring it.

Pleased about the children's choices, Waterford said, "Each of you has chosen a trine sprite gift given to my missing children. Perhaps this is a sign. Maybe you'll find news of them on your quest?"

Carson bowed his head. May had already spoken with the trine sprite Princess Toral. If the princess had no news, how would Carson and his siblings learn anything new? Carson looked up slowly and said, "We'll look for them, Ford. Honest."

When all was ready, Waterford suggested they leave through a gate at the rear of his property to avoid notice. Their spirits high, they made their farewells to Ford with smiles and waves.

Once outside the gate, May led them along a pathway wide enough to allow herself and Robyn to walk in front with the three children following behind. On the town side of the path, they could see the backyards of other houses, some overgrown and others neatly trimmed. In contrast, the other side of the path was fairly thick with trees and shrubs, making it difficult to see more than a few feet into them.

Before too long, a clearing with a small stream appeared. May pointed out the hill in the distance with the new Pointers' Peak at the top. She motioned for them to rest while she withdrew paper and a pencil from her backpack and began making a sketch of the path the children should take to reach the peak. As she drew, she took the binoculars from her pack and viewed the landmarks she wanted to put on her map.

Thinking that perhaps this quest might last into the evening, Carson shuddered as he asked May if this was a possibility. May replied that yes, there was a slight possibility, but not to worry. If it got too late, they could stay in the cave up at the top of the peak. She assured them there were no wing snatchers on the peak itself, and the cave had a sandy floor and space for them to light a fire.

Not comfortable with May's response, Evan asked how far below the peak the wing snatchers lived. May told them their caves were about halfway up, just as the trees started to thin. She got out her binoculars again and asked each of the children to view Pointers' Peak and the terrain leading up to it.

While Marlee studied the map, she asked May why there were no trees on top of the peak. May explained that it could be because the rocks and boulders wouldn't let them grow, or maybe the pointers didn't want them to block their view.

Listening to their words, Robin grew more uncomfortable. "Let's get a move on," she said. "I'll be much happier if we're all together again before night fall."

Δ Δ Δ

Carson's first warning sign came when following the stream bed took longer than May had implied. Many of the rocks were covered in moss and slippery even to their sturdy hiking boots. At one point Evan fell on his behind with a splat after he'd tried to jump too far between the boulders, and yelled about how cold the water felt. May told him that the stream came from an underground spring, making it much colder than the estuary's waters.

Nothing else slowed their progress, as finally they reached the base of the hill and refilled their water bottles from the stream. This was to be their last rest before continuing on their respective journeys.

May sat down heavily with a thump. "Now remember, there are two paths. Your mom and

I are taking the path to the left, as it goes to the old abandoned silver mine. You are taking the path to the right to get to the peak. And, you will be passing close to the new-world home of the trine sprites on your way to the peak."

Then lowering her voice, she said, "Beware the Valley of the Trine. Avoid it unless invited. Remember always that the sprites can be leery of humans, meaning you never know what they'll do when they encounter someone they don't know. However, if you do come across one, look at the color near the edges of its wings—pink for welcoming, blue for thoughtful, gray for sad, and so forth. If the color is red, just stand still and do not approach it."

Carson's Challenge

As soon as they were alone, Carson motioned with his hand for them to stop, then pulled the rough map May had made them from his back pocket. In a whisper, he reminded Evan and Marlee to be as quiet as possible until they got beyond the tree line and the creatures of the forest.

Looking at the map, they reviewed again the three landmarks May had drawn. The first was about a third of the way up the hill at a steep bend in the path, where a large boulder sat with short and fluffy lavender-blue ferns growing at its base. There were two paths at the base of this boulder, and they were to take the one on the right.

The second landmark looked the easiest, but May had warned them to be careful here. Though fewer trees blocked their view, there were several large boulders, meaning that it could be trickier to stay on the path. May had cautioned them to always veer to the right of them, to stay on the true path. If they ever heard the sound of running water, they were going in the wrong direction.

"What kind of a landmark is sound?" whispered Evan.

"As good as any," answered Carson absently. He couldn't help thinking about his dagger and wondering if he could use it if the time came.

The third and last landmark was an old black tree split almost in two, possibly by lightning, a long time ago. By the time they found the tree, the forest should have thinned enough for them to see their way clearly to the peak. This was the only left turn they would make.

Evan thought it looked easy and said as much, while Marlee studied the map long and hard, wishing there was more detail on it. And Carson reminded them to listen for any unusual sounds.

Continuing on their way, they found the first landmark within an hour, and that was when the path got rocky and became more difficult to climb. Evan held Marlee's hand so she wouldn't fall behind while Carson led them forward.

They made a game out of finding the second landmark. It was a smaller boulder shaped like the face of an Indian, complete with headdress and a prominent nose angled to the right. Though walking behind Carson, Evan spotted it first, then pointed it out to Marlee. When they were sure Carson had missed it, they delighted in showing it to him.

Carson chastised himself, scowling at them. He was so intently listening for running water or any other sounds that could mean trouble for them. Then, nodding his head much like their father often did, he ignored his mistake and took the lead once again.

Relieved to reach the third landmark, they turned left, and before long they reached the top. Carson checked his watch, noting they had made the climb in just over three hours, making him more hopeful about getting home before dark.

As they looked at their surroundings, they saw that the peak was oblong in shape, with a few boulders scattered here and there along with some low-lying shrubs. The ground they stood upon consisted of a light-brown sand and dirt spread unevenly over solid bedrock.

Evan spotted the cave first and bent down to enter it. He noted a pile of firewood and what looked to be a few jugs of water against a side wall. There were even several large, smooth stones to sit on around an area that looked like it had been used as a fire pit not too long ago.

The afternoon sun didn't pierce all the way to the back of the cave, so Carson took the flashlight from his backpack to find out where the cave ended. As he did so, Marlee pointed out strange characters on the wall—and again, the language looked to be trine sprite. It seemed similar to the inscriptions on Marlee's bell and Carson's dagger. Shelving of some kind had been carved out of the back wall, and Marlee said these could serve as sleeping benches if they needed them.

Wanting to be down the hill well before dark, Carson led them out of the cave to call Hither and Yon. As they re-emerged into the sunlight, he realized that he hadn't asked May how to do this. Did they whistle? Did they pray? Did they simply call Hither and Yon's together name out loud? Finally, seeing the shadows lengthening on the boulders, Marlee suggested she ring her bell to call May for assistance.

Feeling foolish for not having thought about how to get Hither and Yon to appear, Carson settled on calling Hither and Yon's together name: Time. Marlee and Evan joined him, and they too started calling for Time to appear.

Sensing but not yet seeing a body next to him, Carson dodged left, knocking one of the pointers over. Getting up with some haste and displeasure, Hither dusted off his backside, complaining about humans—and more specifically human children, their clumsiness and lack of tact in general.

Yon smiled benevolently, knowing that their habit of swift movement often had this effect on others. Though he knew these were the MacKenzie children, the rules of the

Beginner had to be observed, so he challenged the children to tell them who was whom.

Ready for this, Carson nodded to Evan to ask the first of several questions they had prepared.

"In the game of hockey, if the puck goes inside the opposing team's net, what happens next?"

Hither replied quickly with a smile, as he had observed this game before. "The point is won, of course."

Yon said, "The next play begins."

So the children easily knew which pointer was which, as Hither spoke of the past—winning the goal—and Yon of the future: starting the next play.

Thus named appropriately, Hither and Yon encouraged the children to ask their questions.

Carson pulled their questions list from his back pocket, along with Queen Annika's request. He nodded to Marlee to begin by reading Queen Annika's request.

"Find the seers Hither and Yon. Once you find them, ask for their assistance in finding a

way to repair the damage done to the house built with the murdered Whimsy tree."

As Marlee finished restating, word for word, Yon shook his head and shrugged his shoulders mumbling under his breath. He looked up and said, "A moment please," as he took Hither aside to confer.

Trying not to laugh out loud, Hither smirked, saying, "Got yourself in a pickle this time I see," as Yon tried to figure out what to tell the children.

Rolling his eyes up to the sky, Yon whispered, "How was I to know this day would actually come? It was just one of many possibilities," he sighed. "And the Beginner has never revealed to me what to tell the children, just that they should come to us for assistance."

"Well we have to tell them something, don't we?" asked Hither, more annoyed than concerned.

Yon turned back to the children with a sincere face. "I can't tell you what to do. I can only guide you."

Stunned, Carson asked, "But what about the prophecy? It said that three children from Captain Jon Dinsmore's bloodline would ask for your assistance in fixing the mean house. We are living in it now, and it needs fixing—bad. It's already bitten Evan and tried to kill Marlee."

"Well I may have told the trine sprites that was one of the possibilities, but it wasn't us who turned what I said into a prophecy. You have to remember that was a terrible night, what with all the burning and murdering going on in town. It isn't good to upset the whimsies, no it isn't," he said with a slow shake of his head. "Perhaps you can help determine which of the visions I saw is the right one? For instance, what do you think could help old Bertie out of the mess he's in?"

"We don't know," wailed Evan. "We're just doing what we were told to do by the dolphin queen."

"Do you always do what you're told, young Evan?" inquired Hither, knowing full well with his gift of hindsight that Evan made up his own rules as he went along.

Silent till now, Marlee quietly said, "I think Lord Ailbert is mean because he's never been loved."

Hither and Yon looked at each other, amazed by her simple statement. Then Hither offered, "That is true, young Marlee. He was cut down in mid-summer, without warning or preparation—murdered, in a sense, and like a poltergeist, he haunts the house built with his wood. Then there was the sad business of Lord Sebastian MacKenzie commanding him to commit all sorts of treacherous acts. That couldn't have helped his disposition, either."

"So all we need to do is get old Bertie to want to un-haunt us, then. Is that right?" Carson asked hopefully.

Slowly nodding his head, Yon said, "It may be that simple."

"But how do you get a house to do that?" Evan asked impatiently.

"That is beyond our knowledge," replied Hither. "Perhaps if you asked the sprites. They live more closely by the Beginner's rules, and after all, they are the whimsies' caretakers."

"But May warned us to avoid them. She said they could be dangerous to humans they don't know," Evan reminded them.

"Wait—I have their bell!" exclaimed Marlee. "I bet if we ring it, they'll come find us. Then we can explain that all we want to do is help Lord Ailbert, not hurt him further."

Wanting to end the discussion and be rid of the children as quickly as he could, Yon agreed that this was an excellent idea and suggested they do so right away.

"We have one more question we promised Ford we'd ask," Carson said quickly, as he saw the pointers starting to back away from them.

Yon nodded to Evan to ask their last unanswered question.

"What happened to Ford's missing family, and how can we get them back to him?"

Hither spoke first, this time saying that the family was still alive and well, at least for the time being.

"But where are they, and how do we get them back to Ford?" Marlee pleaded. "He's so lonely and misses them all so much."

"First thing's first," replied Yon. "Once you have tamed old Bertie, call us again. We are still trying to resolve your other question ourselves. However, though you did not ask it, I can tell you that you are definitely descended from the Dinsmore clan. Your great-aunt Maggie is the sister of the founder of Waters End, Captain Jon Dinsmore."

More confused than ever, Carson said, "That's impossible! Maggie can't have lived that long."

Upset with Carson's tone of voice, Hither gave Carson a warning glance. "It is not our role to solve the problems of the world. We are called upon for advice, and gladly give it to the best of our ability. Calm down and ask yourself how this could be. Has May taught you nothing? Have you never truly listened to the tales of the old country? The answers are in the tales, for they are all true, and everything passed down in them really happened."

Wanting an end to their questions, Yon offered one more piece of information. "Your father may be in grave danger. Did you or did you not leave him home alone in Lord Ailbert?"

With this new worry about their father, Carson was more determined than ever to get them safely down the hill before dark.

Remembering his manners, he thanked Hither and Yon for their time, then said they needed to be on their way if they were to find the Valley of the Trine while the light still held.

Glad to be off the proverbial hook, Hither and Yon waved the children a slight farewell as they began their descent.

"Quite clever of you to say that," Hither whispered with an amused grin while still waving to the children.

"Don't mention it. I swear human children are harder to deal with than the sprites," Hither sighed, then laughed. "And it worked. Let's be off," and as one they vanished from the peak.

A Damsel in Distress

Going down was not as easy as coming up. For one, the shadows cast by the late afternoon sun were long and hid clear sight of the path between the boulders, and Marlee needed more help, as she slid quite often on the loose-pebbled path, slowing them down even further. Though they tried to veer left around the big boulders, before they even approached the second landmark they could already hear the sound of running water, meaning that they had made a wrong turn somewhere.

Deciding they had to get back on course, Carson directed them to veer right at the next large boulder. As they did so, they found the source of the running water. It was not the river below the peak as they had hoped. Instead, it was a tall and narrow waterfall raining heavily down over blue, gray, and green lichen moss-covered rocks of various shapes and sizes.

Though the gorge was only about a dozen feet wide, it seemed to rise up forever. In wonder, they let their eyes travel up to where the sun still glistened at the top.

Evan leaped to the first rock closer into the gorge, then up several more, where there was a dry ledge just big enough for him to stand on and survey their location down the hill. As he was doing this, Carson and Marlee saw what at first glimpse appeared to be another of May's orbs, for it sparkled a full rainbow of colors as it drifted slowly down from the top of the falls.

When the orb reached Evan's location, it appeared to hover slightly above his head. Marlee called out to him to look, and in so doing, he almost lost his balance till his hand found a crevice in the rock wall and he steadied himself once again.

While gazing at the orb, several smaller ones began to form around it. Confused, Carson noticed that the sun was not shining down in the gorge, but only at the top. Yet all three orbs glowed as if the sun's rays were full on them.

"Why are these bubbles hovering over Evan?" Marlee asked.

"Maybe it's because he's in their territory," replied Carson, though he really hadn't any clue as to what they meant.

Trying to reach out and touch the closest orb, Evan could not hear Carson and Marlee's conversation below him. Their voices were muted by the pounding of water over rocks. As Evan finally touched one of the orbs, a shrill scream pierced the air. He could see little in the darkening landscape below them, so he froze, listening intently. When the second scream came, though weaker this time, all three of them realized it as a cry for help.

Evan leapt down from his ledge, and as quietly as they could, they proceeded down the hill toward the sound. As they looked past the last big boulder in their path, they saw a trine sprite flying round and round helplessly, tethered by a long cord to a stake in the ground. When she flew as high as the cord would permit, her wings glimmered iridescently pink and orange as the last of the sunlight touched them, then dulled as she flew lower.

At the entrance to a cave just beyond, they saw a large creature that almost blended in with the rocks around him, so dull and gray was his coloring. The creature was drooling and leering at the poor little sprite. Then a smell wafted over to them, making them gag a bit—which was actually a good thing, because that meant they were downwind of the creature so that it shouldn't be able to smell their presence.

Backing up a few paces behind their protective boulder, they whispered together, trying to figure out what to do. "It's got to be a wing snatcher," said Carson. "He's even uglier than mom described in her stories."

"And that has to be a trine sprite. But look at the dark-gray color on the edges of her wings!" exclaimed Marlee. "She's tiring. We must save her." Both brothers agreed with her. The question was how should they do this.

Evan quickly began picking up pebbles for an old and worn slingshot he had in his backpack.

Pleased, Carson whispered, "Perfecto, Evan! You brought your wrist rocket. If you can distract the wing snatcher by aiming rocks away from us, I can cut the cord with my dagger and free the sprite. Then Marlee can ring her bell once the sprite is free, while I help Evan distract the wing snatcher even further till help arrives."

Though not a perfect plan, as both boys knew they were no match for the wing snatcher, it did seem the best in the moment. Peering around the boulder once again, they could see that the sprite was tiring more, and they knew from their mother's story what would happen to her when she stopped flying on the tether.

Carefully, and as quietly as he could, Evan climbed up the back side of the boulder. He wanted his rocks to appear to land from above the wing snatcher, not from where Carson and Marlee waited to rescue her. *Distraction,* Evan thought, *takes strategy,* and he hoped he was using the right kind.

As the first rock landed, Beezos peered out above his cave. Seeing nothing, he sniffed the air around him, then returned to gloat as the helpless sprite flew slower and lower around the pole.

The plan he and Edward Edwards had made succeeded more easily than Beezos thought it would. He had told Edward where the sprites lived. Together they decided that Edward would walk past the Valley of the Trine carrying a load of silver on his back and talking to himself about harming the MacKenzie children and reclaiming Lord Ailbert. Beezos knew that type of information would send at least one sprite up to the peak to call upon the old seers for advice, and he was ready to catch the sprite as soon as she passed his new cave entrance.

Managing to stay downwind of the creature, Evan set off a few more rocks in quick succession. Beezos looked again at his prize, then scanned the area around him once more.

Seeing and smelling no trouble below him, he left his cave and proceeded around the cliff face to investigate the disturbance above him.

Knowing this was their only chance, Carson darted out from behind the boulder with his dagger drawn. Rushing up to the pole, he cut the tether, freeing the sprite.

Marlee immediately began ringing her bell to draw the sprite to her as they both sought cover in the underbrush farther down the hill.

From the top of the boulder, Evan continued slinging his rocks farther away from the cave's entrance when the creature came upon him from behind. Snatching Evan by his shirt, Beezos shook Evan until his teeth rattled. As Evan tried to call for help, he bit his tongue instead, so fiercely was he tossed to and fro.

Feeling pebbles hit him from above, Carson looked up. All fear for himself forgotten, he scaled the boulder and jumped as high as he could, drawing his blade and stabbing the wing snatcher in the back in one fluid motion.

Stunned at being attacked so, Beezos carelessly dropped Evan over the rim of the boulder and turned to face his new foe.

Waiting with blade drawn, all color drained from Carson's face. Up close, the creature was even bigger, uglier, and more powerful than he could imagine. Carson knew he could not defeat the wing snatcher single-handed, but he knew he had no choice except to try.

"Human children," grunted Beezos, "I'll have you for my supper tonight and the sprite for desert." As he lifted his long, ugly arm towards Carson, Beezos noticed that his sprite was no longer crying for help or flying from her cord beneath them. Enraged, he lumbered off the boulder toward where the sprite should have been, passing Evan's crumpled body on the rocks at its base.

Sniffing wildly at the air, Beezos could find no trace of his prey. Sensing the sprite was out of reach, he roared his displeasure, shaking his clenched claw in the air, giving Carson just enough time to aim and throw his dagger directly at Beezos' heart.

Stunned, Beezos turned, holding his chest with one claw while reaching for Carson with the other. Then he keeled over on top of poor Evan, his green blood oozing out of him as he died.

Jumping down from the boulder, Carson pulled Evan free from under the wing snatcher. Still ringing her bell, Marlee and the trine sprite re-emerged from their hiding space in the shrubbery below and rushed to Evan's side.

"Carson—you did it! You killed the wing snatcher." Marlee beamed at her older brother.

"But I can't wake Evan. He's badly hurt," Carson replied as he gently cradled Evan's head in his lap.

Turning to the sprite, Marlee pleaded, "Can you help Evan?"

Still exhausted from her own ordeal, the sprite smiled weakly. "My people will be here soon. We are in your debt, O children of the prophecy, so sayeth Princess Danika, middle daughter of Queen Arian."

Looking at the princess, Carson held little hope. He blamed himself for Evan's injury and was more frightened than he cared to let Marlee know.

As he looked up to the sky in despair, the darkness seemed to be disappearing, but instead of moon or starlight, he saw an iridescent cloud emitting a rainbow of colors, growing larger by the second and headed straight for them.

A bugle sounded in the distance, followed by the glitter of many pairs of wings descending from above.

The trine sprites landed lithely in a circle surrounding the children, Princess Danika, and the dead wing snatcher. Some touched the ground while others hovered above, creating a kaleidoscope of shimmering color and light.

Princess Danika threw her arms around one of the sprites and sobbed while another, taller sprite stepped forward and bowed low before the children. As if upon command, all the sprites followed suit, silent except for the hum and scratching of many wings, so tightly knit was this convoy of saviors.

Though Carson still sat on the ground, Evan's lifeless head in his lap, he knew this must be the Princess Toral. There was a calmness emanating from within her, and her wings and clothes were a brilliant, almost blinding gold, so brightly did she glow.

Rising from her deep bow, she introduced herself. "Children of the prophecy, on this day we are in your debt, and we thank you for saving our sister. How can we ever repay such courage?"

Carson and Marlee, tears openly streaming down their faces, looked down upon Evan's limp form.

Bending down, Princess Toral laid her hands on Evan's chest, feeling for his heartbeat. As she did so, she sensed his spirit separating from his body. Just in time, she noticed the healing crystal in its pouch around Evan's neck.

Relieved, she spoke with a clear voice, "The Beginner runs strong in this one, and he carries our gift to his cousin on his person."

Taking the crystal from its pouch, she warmed it in her hands, then placed it on Evan's heart while she began a trine sprite healing prayer.

"Beginner before us, Beginner among us, we call on you to heal this brave young warrior.

Beginner of day, Beginner of night, bring back the light of this one's soul.

Beginner of sky, Beginner of air, make whole that which has broken.

Beginner of earth, Beginner of sea, awaken his heart and warm his blood.

Beginner before us, Beginner among us, we call on you to heal this brave young warrior."

As Princess Toral finished the prayer, she saw Evan's spirit sink gently back into his still-lifeless body. Quickly clapping her hands, she bade her strongest sprites to come forth and lift Evan from the ground. "Take him to our valley, to Jen the Healer," she commanded. "I will join you shortly."

At first Carson objected to letting his brother go, until he saw May walking toward them and nodding her head for him to follow Princess Toral's orders. Grim with sadness, he saw his mother right behind May.

Turning towards Carson and Marlee once again, the princess said, "We have done what we can, O children of the prophecy. Take heart, as I saw his spirit re-enter his body, and my people will do their best to help it remain within."

Standing now, openly sobbing and not caring who saw him, Carson watched as over a dozen sprites flew his brother through the darkening sky, the glimmer of their wings lighting his passage. Only when he could no longer see them did he turn to greet May and his mother, their tears glistening with his own.

"Tears are good," said the Princess Danika, quietly approaching the small group. "The Beginner feels them with us. We are never alone. Please know that our healer will tend Evan with our enchanted water, and like our whimsies, growing takes time. Come back to us when the new moon rises. May will guide you."

Turning away swiftly, Princess Danika spat on the ground. "Beezos is dead!" Turning back, she lifted her arms skyward. "Oh Beginner, you have taken one soul today, and though he was our foe, he was part of your plan. Please let us keep the human boy, Evan. He and his brother saved my life today. Hear me now, Beginner of life, for I, the Princess Danika, would take Evan MacKenzie for my third partner in trine."

A hush fell over the gathering, as the naming of a trine partner was sacred indeed. A tall, emerald-winged sprite separated himself from the other earth-bound sprites and approached. "Yes! I, Tristan of the Silver Arrow, approve. We will take this human as our third in trine. His strength matches our own," he finished, bowing his head to the Princess Danika.

In return, the sprites bowed low to both Danika and Tristan, as they knew the tragic tale that had cost this trine their third during the night of the whimsy revolt so long ago. Then they began to sing in happiness as Tristan said, "The name of our original trine was 'Strength.' I think Danika and I have learned that strength alone is not enough to sustain us. Therefore, our new harmony trine name shall be 'Courage.' Long live our trine!"

Lifting his head in newfound hope, Carson smiled and shook Danika and Tristan's hands. "Now I know my brother will live. Thank you, thank you with all my heart," he said with true gratitude. Only then did he turn to face and hug his mother, May, and Marlee. Together they waved their farewells then began their return journey.

Δ Δ Δ

At the base of the hill, Carson heard the stream first and raced to it, falling to his knees as he began to drink the pure, clean water and wash away his dirty tears. Marlee quickly joined him, followed by their mother and May.

Once their thirst was sated and they'd caught their breath, they began their trek for home.

As they walked, Robyn began to describe her and May's adventure trying to locate Edward Edwards. They had found his new entrance to the silver mine and observed the work he had been doing. They could tell he'd dug deeply into a long and wide silver vein, but could find no trace of him. With what he had already taken from the earth, he could be quite wealthy by now.

The hummerling Thor arrived and told them he'd found Edward's house at the end of a rutted lane a little ways outside Waters End. Thor saw Edward loading suitcases into his car, then drive off toward town. He followed him to a large brick building, noting that Edward went inside with several weighty suitcases and came out some time later with only one much smaller case. Edward continued driving out of town. Thor debated following him, then decided to return with what news he did have.

Not caring about Edward at the moment, Marlee asked Carson if he really felt Evan would live.

With a newfound knowing, Carson turned and said to all of them, "Yes! Evan will live, but what about Dad? Yon said something about danger that we left Dad alone with Lord Ailbert."

In haste once again, they rushed for home.

HOME ALONE

Thinking his family away at May's beach house for the weekend, Nelson breathed a sigh of relief. For the first time since they'd moved to Dolphin Court, he had the house to himself.

After cleaning up the leftover breakfast dishes, he poured himself a cup of hot, black coffee and wandered around the house a bit, looking for anything that needed tidying up.

Wandering upstairs, he walked through his children's rooms. As expected, Marlee's was neat and tidy, but the boys' rooms were a war zone. While avoiding stepping on toys, games, and piles of clothing, a movement outside the window of Evan's bedroom caught his eye. A flash of bright color darted through the bushes at the end of his overgrown backyard.

Not certain of what he saw, his curiosity was piqued. *Aha!* he thought as he quickly decided to begin his weekend alone by cleaning up the rear yard first.

Marching through the kitchen door and turning left a few paces, he opened the door of an old but tidy tool shed, complete with work table and benches. Flicking the light switch as he entered, he saw a rather large spider sitting on his work bench. He could tell it wasn't a black widow, as it didn't have the long, knobby knees or shiny body, and its color kept shifting.

Though its legs were long like a daddy long-legs, its body was translucent and shaped like a perfect pear diamond, similar to the one he'd given Robyn in her engagement ring. But at over two inches in body size alone, it was much bigger than Nelson liked.

He turned and grabbed a thick leather glove off the hook to the right of the door. When he looked back a split-second later, the spider was gone. Letting his eyes move around the shed then upward, he saw it on the ceiling, scurrying into a crevice he could not easily reach.

Smiling to himself, he decided he'd set off an insect fogger soon. He took the other glove off its hook, picked up several garden tools for cutting branches and whacking weeds, and walked back outside to get started cleaning up his rear yard.

A few hours later, he had finally cleared a path through to the end of his property. He was disappointed to see no sign of the big, brightly-colored bird he thought he had seen from Evan's window. Thinking all his hacking and chopping must have scared it off, he made a mental note to look for it another day.

After cleaning up and making himself an early dinner, he poured himself another cup of coffee and took it to his new study at the front of the house, pacing as if undecided which work project to tackle first. Feeling a sudden chill, he struck a long match and lit the kindling in the old-but-functional fireplace, then he continued pacing.

His old, high-backed leather desk chair looked so inviting that he sat in it, hoping this would clear his mind for work. The thick, scrolled wooden arms were smooth with years of wear, reminding him of the day he received it as a gift from Robyn and the kids.

Pausing, he remembered how excited he was to graduate from college, then find a job with a successful company specializing in commercial building design. As he and Robyn were best friends through their college years, it only made sense to him that they marry and start raising a family upon graduation, but this last move to Waters End seemed to have unnerved not just his wife, but his three children as well.

This was the third town they'd moved to over the last dozen years as his job responsibilities and promotions increased, and though he knew the children were at an age where they needed to settle into one place for a while, he struggled with their lack of cooperation.

Pacing again, his thoughts turned to questions. Was his wife going goofy on him, or worse yet, had she fallen out of love with him?

Didn't she remember they had agreed that she would handle family matters so that he could provide the money they needed to live comfortably, put the children in the right schools, and buy them the necessities they needed to learn and grow up well in today's society?

Confused, he shook his head and found he couldn't concentrate on his work just yet. He wanted to understand why his family disliked this beautiful home he'd bought them and why they were so unappreciative of all his efforts to provide well for them.

Why was Robyn always making that sniffling sound whenever he would make even the simplest of requests? Why was Carson giving him a stone-faced stare whenever he suggested his eldest son do something, and why did Evan and Marlee appear to talk to him only through their mother?

Slowly shaking his head, trying to clear it, he found himself staring at the window instead. He did not see anything out of it, as his eyes were still focused inward. He didn't notice anything on it, either, or he would have seen the same long-legged spider he'd seen earlier in the day in the garden shed perched on the sill and looking right at him, sharing his same perplexed look.

Like Lord Ailbert, the spider wanted to know what this new family of MacKenzies was up to. Watching Nelson, the spider sensed neither magical powers nor cruelty, and this didn't make sense, as all the families that had owned Lord Ailbert were devious and not to be trusted.

Lost in thought, Nelson did not see the spider trapeze her web over to his desk and land there, still and cautious. Building up its courage, it gradually moved closer to the lid of Nelson's small black computer.

"Ahem!" said the spider as it cleared its throat.

Nelson appeared not to have heard and kept staring at the window.

Louder this time, the spider inquired rather imperiously, "Mr. MacKenzie, I presume?"

Startled, Nelson looked toward the doorway. As the room came back into focus, he saw no one at the door or anywhere else in the room. "Whoever you are, would you stop clearing your throat?" said Nelson to the room at large. "It sounds disgusting, like you have a bad cold or something. And I don't believe in ghosts, so whatever your point is, make it fast."

The voice spoke with mounting impatience this time. "Are you or are you not Mr. MacKenzie, the new owner of Lord Ailbert?"

Not willing to answer a voice without a body, Nelson continued looking from whence the sound came.

Finally, the by-then-irritated spider took a chance and proclaimed rather loudly, "I'm right here by your laptop, you dunce! Are you daft?" it added at the last, thinking this human may be hard of hearing.

In disbelief, Nelson looked down at his keyboard and saw the same iridescent spider that had eluded him earlier that day. Though his instinct was to squash it immediately, he couldn't. Amazing as it seemed, this spider had just spoken to him, and it had the most beautiful almond-shaped eyes. *Who ever thought of a spider's eyes?* he wondered.

"That's better," said the spider, happy to have Nelson's attention at last—and noting that he did not appear to be about to do harm as he had during their first encounter.

"Let me introduce myself, then," it continued, raising up to a standing position on four of its eight legs, then curtseying by slightly bending its lower legs and spreading its uppers out wide as if they were holding up a skirt, and a luminescent one at that, as it appeared to glow through its movements.

"My name is Melinda," the spider pronounced carefully and evenly to make sure he got it right. "And I, like generations before me, live with Lord Ailbert. He provides us with a home. In turn, we keep him bug-free. You may have noticed the lack of termites in his wood, or noted that none of you have been bitten by mosquitoes since you arrived. And no matter how often your children leave the doors open or the screens up, have you ever seen a fly in this house?"

Deciding he must be dreaming, Nelson replied, "Come to think of it, I haven't. And as you already appear to know my name, I suppose I don't need to introduce myself. But how can a spider talk to me?"

Insulted, Melinda almost spat at him, "Have you ever spoken to a spider before?"

Dumbfounded, Nelson just stared at her.

"Spiders can't talk. I am a *spa*-lider," she said, emphasizing the first syllable. "Of all the spiders in this world, only we have the gift of communication among all living beings. The Beginner made us and gifted us so, and that is the way it is."

Giving in completely to the dream for now, Nelson said, "Okay, fair enough. But who is Lord Ailbert?"

Astonished, Melinda replied, "How can you not know of Lord Ailbert? Your own kinsman slew him without warning or permission."

"My own what killed who?" Nelson questioned, pinching himself hard to wake up now. When that had no effect, he asked more slowly and politely to which relation Melinda was referring.

"Why, Lord Sebastian MacKenzie, the cruelest bastard to have ever lived," Melinda almost shouted.

While Nelson stared blankly at Melinda, she asked, "Do you not know your own heritage?" Then, trying another tact, asked, "Where were you born?"

"I was raised in a small college town a few days drive north and west of here. I know of a Lord Robert MacKenzie of the old country in my family tree, but never have I heard of a Lord Sebastian MacKenzie."

Watching him carefully, Melinda decided he was telling the truth, and more importantly, that he was descended from the good Lord MacKenzie and not his evil cousin. Relieved, she said, "At least Waterford will be happy to learn of this."

"Waterford?" Nelson responded uncertainly as he imagined the fine crystal goblets in their butler's pantry. Looking at Melinda cautiously, Nelson asked, "Is Lord Ailbert a type of glass, then?"

Understanding his confusion, Melinda giggled. "Perhaps if you are referring to his windows, but he is much more than that. Lord Ailbert is the name of this house, and he is alive. Aren't you, Ailbert?" she finished as a humming, rumbling sound began, followed by a shaking so strong she could barely hold onto the desk, so she took to the air dangling from a glistening web cord, swinging back and forth right in front of Nelson's shocked face.

"Silence, spalider!" commanded Lord Ailbert into their minds.

Shaken from his chair and onto the floor, Nelson looked for the source of this new voice.

Though the house had ceased shaking, the fireplace and lights were still flickering on and off. Stunned, Nelson remained quietly on the floor, drawing his legs under him in a crosswise position and wondering what a healthy Lord Ailbert might do.

Dust bunnies floated through the air as the lights returned to normal once again. Melinda landed on Nelson's desk, then quickly took charge. "Lord Ailbert, it is so good to have you awake and among us again. Let me introduce you to Mr. Nelson MacKenzie of the Lord Robert MacKenzie side of the family," she finished, emphasizing the particular branch of the family.

Lord Ailbert creaked, then moaned low in response.

Finding all this rather difficult to grasp, Nelson spoke up, "House...err...Lord Ailbert, how can you talk?" Then, mumbling partly to himself and still loud enough for Lord Ailbert and Melinda to hear, "First a spider talks to me, and now a house? This is beyond belief. It's as if the old myths were true, but that's impossible, for they were and are only faery tales." Nelson shook his head strongly from left to right, then up and down, almost the same way Evan did.

Surprised once more that this new human resident showed no signs of trying to control him, Lord Ailbert could not understand this family. He had never seen such love and caring between humans before, reminding him of his yearning for his beloved Isabelle back in the old forest of his youth.

He could still hear her screams—then, just as he was trying to untangle his own roots from the ground, the tree cutters came for him too. He was helpless—he couldn't save her or himself. All the little saplings they'd planned were never to be born!

Moaning aloud, Lord Ailbert sobbed. He cried so hard that the house shook almost from its foundation, and the fire sprinklers launched, so violently did he jolt to and fro in his anguish.

As the ceiling rained, he spoke aloud, "Ah, Beginner help me! Why was I made to suffer so?" he asked as his anguish turned to whimpers and finally to moans as he quieted. And as he rested, the rain ceased and Nelson and Melinda could move about again.

"There, there," comforted Melinda. "I know how much you've suffered, Lord Ailbert, for the tales have come down to me through my own kinsmen. But this man knows nothing of your history. Perhaps if you were to open up, if you were to finally talk about it after all this time, you could let it go?"

"It's too painful," cried the house into their minds with such force as to knock Nelson down once more and to send Melinda dangling.

"Please, for your own sake," she pleaded from a lopsided position as she swung to and fro.

"I was cut down in my prime, with no winter solstice ceremony to prepare me for my next life, no permission asked nor granted," wailed Lord Ailbert so loud his windows shook, and Nelson felt it prudent to remain on the floor a while longer.

"Yes, yes, we know that part. And there is more," Melinda gently encouraged him.

"I don't know where to begin," he moaned softer now, his sorrow and confusion evident in his voice.

"What happened to Isabelle?" asked Melinda cautiously, trying to draw him out.

"How did you know of her?" demanded Lord Ailbert, his voice full of suspicion.

"The first Lady Sebastian wrote about Isabelle in her journals. It seems you had at least one other human living with you who tried to take care of you."

"Oh well," he sighed. "Isabelle never awoke, though I overheard Lord Sebastian say that the trees who refused to awaken were turned into furniture and house trimmings. I've always wondered which pieces she could have been turned into, and if any were inside me. Was she in some form still with me? As such, I've taken great care with all my windows and doors, beds, sideboards, and tables just in case any of them were made from her."

"Have you never asked the trine sprites for help, then?" asked Melinda. "You know, they might be able to awaken her still."

"The blasted sprites were not here when I was built, and though they have approached me these last hundred years, I will not speak to them now. They awakened me, then forsook me. I am done with the faeries of old."

"Dear Lord Ailbert," sighed Nelson, "my family was against our moving into you. Somehow they sensed your pain and unhappiness where I did not. We had spent weeks looking for a suitable home. You are the only house in this whole town that met my requirements. I do not mean any disrespect for what you have gone through, and I know that my family and I will appreciate you, take care of you, and help you as best we can. Our clan is not the clan of my forbearer's disturbed cousin."

Then, stronger, his own anguish showing, Nelson continued, "And I myself am troubled these days. I love my family and feel I'm losing them, and I don't know why. Someone has to be responsible. Someone needs to look after them, yet they are increasingly ignoring me. I work hard—I always have. Is the result of hard work losing everyone who ever mattered to you?" Nelson ended on his own sob as he began to shake with his own tears.

"I wondered why you were so sad," Melinda said as she swung directly in front of Nelson's face, forcing him to back up a step and trip over the chair right behind him, landing on it and then the floor with the chair on top of him. "Let me weave you a web of happiness, then, for your family does still love you so. And Lord Ailbert, I think it is high time you realize this is a good and loving family. They will do right by you."

All of a sudden, Lord Ailbert began to laugh. Then he laughed out loud, arching his windows into a big smile.

"What's so funny?" countered Nelson as he tried to extract himself from the chair and the floor once more, then immediately fell down again as Lord Ailbert's laughter rocked the house almost as much as his sadness had.

"Why, Nelson MacKenzie, can you never stay on your feet?" joked the house.

"Not with all this shaking going on, Bertie," grinned Nelson from the floor.

Growing still once more, Lord Ailbert said, "No one's called me that name for many a year, and I used to dislike it. But now it somehow makes me feel good—younger, in fact. I've made up my mind, then. You and your family can live with me," he ended rather smugly.

Pleased, Nelson thanked Lord Ailbert while Melinda did indeed weave a web of happiness up in the corner of the study across from the fireplace, its strands glistening pink, red, and orange in the flickering fire's light.

Reunited

Unlike at the beginning of their adventure, the remaining questers paid little heed to the forest creatures of the night, or the beautiful moon that had risen since their departure.

"What are we going to tell your father?" worried Robyn as they raced along the streambed, sometimes in it more than on top of its rocks and sandy borders. May tried to console her as Carson and Marlee raced ahead, more surefooted than their elders.

"I just want Dad to be okay," said Carson to the wind.

"He will be, Carson. I just know it," panted Marlee, struggling to keep up with him.

Tired, dirty, and afraid, Carson—with Marlee in tow—began calling for their father even before they slammed into and through Lord Ailbert's front door. Seeing their father on the floor with a large spider dangling above him, they immediately thought the worst.

Just as Carson was pulling out his dagger and Marlee her bell, Melinda spoke. "What's the hurry, little ones?" Then, as she saw Carson approach her with the dagger in his right hand, she bungee-jumped to the ceiling, calling to Nelson to protect her.

"Carson!" yelled his father. "What are you doing with a dagger in your hand in our home?"

"But Dad," wailed Carson, "that spider was attacking you!"

"She was what?" answered Nelson, forgetting for the moment that his family had not yet met Melinda.

"Melinda is not a spider, Carson. She is a *spa*-lider," he said, emphasizing the first syllable just as Melinda had done. "And she is an intelligent one at that." Finally untangling himself from the chair and the floor, he asked Melinda to come down.

Cautiously she dropped down and landed on Nelson's shoulder, her eyes glowing large as she warily watched the children.

"It seems I finally know something that you do not," chuckled their father as Melinda almost purred into his left ear.

"Allow me to introduce you, then. Carson and Marlee, meet Melinda, spalider extraordinaire."

Humming with pleasure at Nelson's compliment, Melinda arched up on her four lower legs and bowed deeply to the children.

"The pleasure is all mine," she said as she returned to her more natural stance.

"But Dad," insisted Carson, "Hither and Yon said you were in grave danger. What were we supposed to think?"

"Carson, didn't you learn anything from Maggie's tales? Never consort with pointer pairs. They send mixed messages." But no sooner were the words out of his mouth than he began to laugh again. "Nothing can amaze me now. Who would have believed that the old tales were true—every one of them?"

As he finished, Robyn and May stood in the doorway, smiling for the first time that day. Robyn rushed up to Nelson and gave him a huge bear hug and sloppy kiss as Melinda jumped shoulders to May and introduced herself.

Melinda cleared her throat again as she thought to Bertie that he needed to introduce himself as well.

Enjoying the confusion around him, Bertie flicked the lights and the fireplace on and off a few times to get their attention. As they stilled and looked around, he spoke aloud, "Never have I been fortunate enough to have such love and fun within my walls. Welcome home, young ones. Your father and I have had a long discussion, and yes, I would like you all to continue living with me."

Then, softer and into their minds, he whispered, "Oh, and call me Bertie. Somehow Lord Ailbert doesn't seem appropriate anymore."

Beaming at his family, Nelson suddenly missed Evan. As the question began to form on his lips, May rushed to the rescue. "There's been a bit of a to-do with a wing snatcher this day, and Evan's being well cared for by the trine sprites. They are giving him their enchanted water, and he should be right as rain shortly."

The incredulity of their situation stunned him once again. "What did happen to Evan, and why aren't you all at May's beach house?"

"It's a rather long story, dear," said his wife as she backed up and looked him in the eye beseechingly. She began describing the events he had had no knowledge of since that fateful day when they first met Waterford, then the royal dolphins, and finally the trine sprites.

Carson and Marlee kept interjecting their own versions of what happened, along with

Marlee's experience with Want-Not and Waste-Not.

At one point, May and Melinda called them all into the kitchen for hot chocolate and biscuits, as she knew they were thirsty and famished.

Winding down their adventure, they finally came to the part about the battle with Beezos the wing snatcher, and how brave Evan had been, and Carson as well for killing it before it got them all.

Giving Carson a steady stare, his father shook his hand. "That took a lot of guts, son. I am proud of you. In fact, I am proud of my whole family." He smiled at them benevolently.

Garbanzo Waffles

The next morning, Carson and Marlee were up first and into the kitchen. They made their father's favorite garbanzo bean waffles with toasted almonds, fresh berries, cottage cheese, and hot maple syrup. That is, they made it with Lord Ailbert's help.

Shocked that Carson hadn't learned to cook even the basics, Bertie asked him to read the recipe out loud, then supervised its preparation, as even the differences between low, medium, and high heat were beyond Carson's understanding.

Marlee cooked the bacon just under crisp, as she knew it would go in the oven to stay warm while she cut up fresh strawberries and rinsed the just-picked wild blueberries from the backyard.

Bertie also showed them how to brew a pot of coffee using a French press, as he knew their father preferred strong black coffee over the breakfast tea the rest of his family drank.

Delighted, Robyn and Nelson thanked Bertie for teaching their children how to cook.

All of a sudden Bertie was embarrassed, as he did not know how to handle a compliment.

"Thank you again, Lord Ailbert—I mean Bertie," beamed Marlee. "And thank you for the bedtime story last night, too."

Dismayed at being left out, Carson asked, "What story? Why didn't I get one as well?"

"Maybe if you learn how to cook, Bertie will tell you one, too. Right, Bertie?" she laughed. Then, smiling widely at her family, "Maybe I did learn something from Waste-Not and Want-Not after all."

"What's that, kiddo?" asked Nelson.

"Oh, just that if I can see it in my mind, then I can make it happen." Marlee grinned, remembering how Want-Not had helped her to use her imagination to picture what she wanted more than anything else in the whole wide world.

"Perhaps the pointer pairs aren't all bad news then, eh?" replied Nelson, tousling her hair, his own equally wide grin turning into a soft, loving smile.

"If only Evan was here," sighed Carson as he finished off his second helping of waffles.

Nelson looked at the drooping faces of his family, then tried to cheer them up. "Two weeks and we'll get him back stronger than ever. Just you wait and see. I for one have never heard of a trine sprite that can't cure anything or anyone they set their hearts on healing!"

WAITING IS...

Each member of the MacKenzie family struggled while waiting for news of Evan. What surprised them was how much their new home, Lord Ailbert, also struggled. Like a worried uncle, he was constantly chattering to whoever would listen to him.

"Can the trine sprites get him to eat? They must feed him their enchanted water, at the least. Do you know if they will do that? When I was a young tree, it helped me to learn how to think and reason; it helped me to grow into the beautiful, strong tree that I was before...well, before the tree cutters came..."

Then Bertie would become sullen, remembering all the bad things he'd experienced, and be silent for a while. No amount of cajoling would budge him when this happened, and so the family spoke quietly amongst themselves and waited.

Δ Δ Δ

The next Saturday, May arrived unexpectedly after her morning shift, insisting that Nelson meet Waterford.

Ford's first reaction upon meeting Nelson was disappointment, followed by a quick acceptance. Ford could see that yes, this family did have a father after all, and one who cared deeply for them.

In turn, Nelson was intrigued to learn of Ford's missing family and asked him to tell him his story from the beginning. Then he too hunted through Ford from the basement all the way to the third floor, looking for clues just as his family and May had been doing for some time.

River Dance

Halfway through the wait for Evan's return, May and Robyn packed them all a picnic lunch and took Nelson to the sandy cove at the end of the park.

When Nelson stopped to smell the wild white gardenias, he was amazed to overhear and understand a conversation between two glistening white hummingbirds in the next bush. Intrigued by their size and unusual color, he was also confused by their conversation. They were saying something about the king and queen of the sea.

As they darted away, he shook his head, wondering what this meant. Then he joined his family at the old wooden picnic table, excited to share his encounter. Carson and Marlee laughed out loud as their mother, and May grinned. When their father asked what was so funny, they were silent, knowing that their father had just sent a pair of hummerlings to call the royal dolphins, and they wondered which dolphin would appear this time.

On cue, as they were passing around sandwiches and potato salad, a pair of fins appeared offshore, then rolled near the cove side by side. Carson and Marlee jumped up from the table and ran into the water up to their waists as their father let out a yell of fear, thinking sharks had come up the estuary.

When he saw the two dolphins lift their heads from the water and nicker at his children, he dashed to the water's edge himself, kicking off his flip-flops and getting as close as he dared.

"Welcome to the real world at last, father MacKenzie," said Queen Annika into all their minds as she motioned to Nelson with her snout. She introduced herself and her life partner, King Koru.

"Was it you who led Captain Dinsmore to Waters End?" Nelson asked, remembering the myth about the founding of the town.

"Yes," replied King Koru, "and we had several others with us at the time. In fact, we also led your direct ancestor Lord Robert MacKenzie and his family to this exact spot. He anchored his ship, Old Letty, near this inlet, as the pier south of here had yet to be built."

"Wonderful!" exclaimed Nelson, clapping his hands together. "It is so good to meet you and to know that you are real, for I have always loved the sea and wished I had taken the time to learn how to sail on her."

The two dolphins nickered between themselves for a moment, then the queen swam next to Carson and Marlee, requesting they get on her back behind her dorsal fin. King Koru invited Nelson up onto his back. "Let us give you your first taste of sailing, then."

Turning quickly toward his wife and May, they smiled and waved their hands in mock farewell, similar to the way he'd dismissed them just the week before when he thought they were going to May's beach cottage for the weekend. For the first time in years, he felt the joy of his own childhood returning.

Then, doing as he was bid, Nelson walked out farther into the cove until he was deep enough to grab King Koru's dorsal fin and slide onto his back. Carson and Marlee were already out in mid-channel on Queen Annika's back, laughing as she glided smoothly through the small waves caused by the swift-moving current and the afternoon breeze.

When King Koru caught up with them, Carson declared a race to the huge boulder known as Bird Rock across from Pointers' Peak, about a mile up-river. Daring each other in turn, the king and queen of the sea thoroughly enjoyed themselves as well, with first one, then the other pulling ahead.

With the spray from the wavetops in their eyes, the MacKenzies had to squint to see where they were and who was really in the lead at any one time. Then suddenly their pace changed, and it appeared the dolphins were pulling out all the stops as their speed more than doubled.

Marlee was no longer happy. She was having trouble holding onto Queen Annika's dorsal fin even though Carson told her to grip the sides of the dolphin harder with her knees. Just when she thought she could hang on no longer, Queen Annika unceremoniously launched them from her back and onto another sandy inlet about a quarter mile short of their intended destination.

Stunned, they watched the queen of the sea swim back and circle King Koru, who still had their father on his back. Then she dove under him. A few seconds later, they saw a huge bull shark tossed up in the air. As it landed back in the water, she rammed it full on its side. King Koru quickly dropped Nelson off at the beach, where his children stood in awe watching the queen attack the shark. Then he swam to her side. A second bull shark surfaced, and it appeared some type of conversation was taking place between the dolphins and the sharks.

As the sharks sped away down the estuary and toward the sea, the king and queen returned to the beach and bade the children and their father return to their backs.

"I didn't know sharks could swim in rivers," Carson mumbled, unsure of returning to Queen Annika's back.

Understanding, she nickered and said in their minds, "There are several species of shark that can and do swim in all the ocean bound waterways of this world, whether they are of salt or fresh water. These two bull sharks were vying for our attention, but with you on our backs, we did not feel comfortable and let them know that they were not welcome here today."

"Sharks can be wily," added King Koru. "This pair knew they were not permitted in these waters, but they saw us arrive, and they had news they wanted to share with us. They will not be back soon," he chuckled, making a melodious coughing sound. "Come! Let us finish our race."

Nelson declined with a grin, saying that perhaps he'd learn how to sail a boat first next time.

Both Carson and Marlee agreed and requested that the dolphins return them to their cove instead of finishing the race. After all, they now knew how fast the dolphins could swim if they were really racing, so the game was not as much fun.

As they approached their cove once more, May and Robyn were standing by the water waiting for them. Once Carson related their adventure to May, she nickered to the dolphins in their own language for a few minutes, then all said farewell as the king and queen sped back into the open channel and out to sea once more.

"Come sit at the table for a bit, and let's finish our lunches," May requested.

When all were seated again, she told them about the private conversation she and the dolphins had. "There's something strange going on, what with those sharks in our estuary. Though the dolphins were happy to learn that you have made a friend of Lord Ailbert, they informed me of what the sharks told them, that Edward Edwards has purchased a large ship and hired a crew to take him to the old country. They overheard this yesterday evening while following a particularly enticing school of sea bass near the pier where the ship was being provisioned."

"Well isn't this good news, then?" asked Nelson.

"Actually, what the sharks heard was the crew addressing our Mr. Edwards as Lord MacKenzie," May replied.

As the MacKenzies looked at her in confusion, she reminded them of Lord Ailbert's origin at the hands of Lord Sebastian MacKenzie.

"But why would he be calling himself Lord MacKenzie?" Carson asked, irritated that Edward Edwards would take on their last name. "And why is he going to the old country?"

"The dolphins are investigating that now and will let us know when they have more information."

"Carson, let's add this to our questions list, as we now have another mystery to solve," Marlee added.

"Okay," he replied, "but first thing's first— we need Evan back whole and with us again. Our own trine isn't the same without him."

For once, Carson wasn't hungry. He kept seeing Evan's crumpled body under Beezos, the wing snatcher he'd killed while saving the trine sprite Princess Danika from certain death.

Homecoming

Finally the afternoon of the new moon approached. Though only two weeks had passed, it seemed much longer. As the family readied for their trek to the Valley of the Trine, Bertie began fussing over them.

"Did you remember to pack fresh clothes for Evan? What about some tea or his favorite root beer? I don't know what the sprites eat or drink. What if their food isn't good for him?"

May walked in the front door just as Bertie finished asking Robyn this last question and twisted completely around twice looking for her. She finally saw Robyn at the top of the stairs, trying to get the rest of her family downstairs. After promising they'd be ready soon, May settled into a comfy overstuffed chair to wait.

Smiling, she informed Bertie that the sprites eat similarly to humans, except they do not buy their food in a store. They grow their own herbs, grains, fruits, nuts, and vegetables.

Bertie was quiet as he thought about what May said, so she continued, "Have you seen what grows in Ford's garden?"

"No human ever loved me before," Bertie sighed.

"Loving can be learned, Bertie. And your happiness level will grow the more you practice. Right, Nelson?" she said aloud as the family walked down the stairs.

Nelson smiled while Marlee hugged him, so glad was she to be retrieving Evan from the trine sprites.

Hastily they bid farewell to Bertie, then drove directly to the base of Pointers' Peak, where May took the lead with Carson right beside her.

Dry from the hot summer, their progress up the hill was noisy as they stepped on crackling brush, while pebbles slid under their feet. As they neared the final bend in the path, two sprites were already waiting for them, hovering a few feet above the ground, their wings sparkling in the sunlight.

Carson recognized the two sprites, as the Princess Danika had run to them after he had killed the wing snatcher. They were smiling—a good sign, he hoped. Then, looking at them more closely, he realized they were identical twins.

"Welcome, May and MacKenzies," the sisters said in unison. They introduced themselves as Pearl and Zinnia, younger sisters of the Princess Danika. "We are honored by your presence and will guide you to our home."

Both sprites landed on either side of Carson, each taking a hand and thanking him again for killing the wing snatcher and saving their sister's life. Embarrassed by their attention, Carson couldn't think of anything to say, and grinned shyly in return.

Soon their path stopped abruptly before a wall of thick, gnarled vines climbing down from the mountainside. The sisters bowed to the vines. In response, the vines opened so all could pass through the tunnel entrance to the Valley of the Trine Sprites. Hovering again, the sprites' wings provided enough light to walk through the tunnel.

Still in the lead, Carson was the first to see the Valley of the Trine spread out before him. His eyes immediately went to the waterfall in the distance, and he knew from the tales that this was where they were headed.

As the rest of his family exited the tunnel, Nelson placed Marlee on his shoulders so that she too could see the valley below. They marveled at the heavily forested valley, and taller than any others were the whimsy trees closest to the waterfall.

The path down to the waterfall was cleanly swept, and easy to follow with gentle bends and few obstacles, plus Pearl and Zinnia continued to lead them down by fluttering above and just beyond them.

As they neared the valley floor, the whooshing sound of the waterfall and the mist it created slightly obscured their view. Walking to the far end, they came upon a ceremony of sorts, with Evan standing tall and proud in the middle of it all, many trine sprites seated quietly around him.

Evan smiled widely as they approached, waving his hello.

"Mom, Evan's grown taller these last few weeks," Carson said. "Could it be the water from the sprites' pond?"

Pearl and Zinnia answered "yes" for Robyn then put their fingers to their lips, asking them to listen and wait. Evan was not only fully recovered, he had found his trine and was being initiated into it before going home to his family.

Smiling her welcome to the MacKenzies, the Princess Toral raised her arms as a soft drum began to beat.

"There are only two rules in this universe among awakened beings:

1) You will be kind.

2) You will love.

So sayeth the Beginner of Us All to each as we are born. Too many forget. Too many others block the message entirely, experiencing only one or the other as they grow. And sadly, some never experience either.

These rules cannot stand alone. They cannot be divided, for there is no love without kindness, and there is no kindness without love.

Harken to my words, O children of the Earth. There are but two rules, and the mission of Princess Toral and the harmony trine known as Pax is to spend the rest of our days spreading this truth."

The sprites then echoed the princess chanting the two rules several times until once again she raised her arms and said, "Let the new harmony trine ceremony commence!"

Proudly, Tristan of the Silver Arrow and the Princess Danika took their places on either side of Evan. The three of them formed a circle, staring each in the eye they began their pledge. One by one they uttered the sacred words, with the Princess Danika saying her pledge first:

"I give myself in trine to Tristan of the Silver Arrow and to Evan MacKenzie as my trine partners for life.

Together, we three are more of what the Beginner has called upon us to be. In coming together in harmony, we do not forsake our families, for they are sacred. Each piece of us belongs to another, and no one piece belongs to any except to the Beginner who made us all.

In trine we become stronger. In trine, we share our special and unique gifts, one with the other. We have named our trine 'Courage,' for together we can face any adversity with a passionate heart, with the physical strength of a sea collie, and with the mental clarity of a lightning hawk.

Long live our trine!"

Tristan of the Silver Arrow repeated the pledge, followed by Evan. Once they finished, Danika and Tristan wrapped their arms around Evan's shoulders. As one the three began to float up to the top of the waterfall, then stood for all to see. In an act of courage, all three dove down into the pool and swam to the edge, emerging with broad smiles.

The Princess Toral approached them benevolently, "To the harmony trine known as Courage. Let us now celebrate with a harmony trine feast!"

As cheers and well wishes broke out, Carson was the first to reach Evan, and the brothers hugged long and tightly. There would be time for words later, once Evan was home again. For now, they would celebrate Evan's return to health and his new trine family.

Δ Δ Δ

On their way home, Carson asked Evan about his trine partner pledge. "What's a sea collie and a lightning hawk? They aren't in any of the old tales we've heard."

Evan said, "I hope to meet them someday myself. Danika said they were beloved by her people back in the old country. Both have great courage, which is why they were chosen as our pledge symbols."

What other characters from the old world have we yet to meet wondered Carson, then pushed the thought aside as he said, "And you're as tall as I am now Evan."

"Almost," Evan replied with a grin punching Carson in the arm first for once.

"Did the sprites feed you their enchanted water?" Carson asked in awe.

"They may have," replied Evan. "I don't remember the first few days I was with them."

"If so, I wonder if you will live longer because of it too? I mean, remember what the pointers said up on the peak when I asked how could Aunt Maggie live so long?"

"Let's ask May," Evan replied. "I feel stronger than ever before. Another question for our list, eh?"

Catching up to, and then hugging both brothers at once, Marlee asked Evan what the sprites were like.

"They are just like in mom's tales, only kinder," he replied. "And they do laugh and like to have fun. Maybe I get to see another side of them because I am part of a harmony trine with them. Now that was truly amazing."

Thoughtful and still concerned, Marlee asked, "But what about our trine, the Mackenzie trine Evan?"

"That will never change Marlee bo-barley," Evan said teasing her as he ruffled the hair on top of her head. "Maybe you'll find a second trine yourself someday."

Poof!

Visiting Ford again a few days later, Carson, Evan, and Marlee found May and Danika in the kitchen. While Marlee helped May prepare some snacks, Evan, Carson, and Danika walked through Ford's rooms again, looking for anything else Ford may have missed.

As they approached the parlor near the front of the house, Danika asked, "Ford, why haven't you repaired the cracked glass in your parlor doors?"

Surprised, Ford said, "I don't remember seeing those cracks before. I'll fix them immediately."

Excited, Evan said, "Good job, Danika. We finally have something else Ford doesn't remember. Carson, let's get the list from the other room. We've finally got another clue."

Once they'd left, Danika admired how prettily the bevel-cut glass panes sparkled in the afternoon light. "Thank you, Ford. These doors are beautifully crafted." She opened them both and walked inside the parlor to study the crystal prism hanging by the window, glowing softly in the morning light. As she studied it, she knew she'd seen it before, but from where she could not immediately remember.

Returning to the parlor with their clue list, Carson poked his head in looking for Danika. She was nowhere to be found. "Ford, where'd Danika go?"

"She's still in the parlor," answered Ford. "I would have noticed had she left, really I would."

"Maybe she's playing hide and seek?" Carson said to Ford right as Evan came up. "Evan, you take the upstairs. I'll check down here," he finished as he raced first to the back of the house, then down through Ford's large basement rooms.

Not finding her anywhere, Carson was a bit frustrated, so he returned to the parlor and walked inside. While looking behind the furniture, a reflection of light from the crystal prism dangling near the window caught his eye. Then looking up at it directly, he too vanished from the room.

ODDS AND ENDS

EXCERPT FROM BOOK 2

"Ouch!" cried Carson as he landed on his bum on a hard wooden surface. Confused and disoriented, he struggled to stand up, only to discover that the rocking motion beneath his feet was real.

He took a careful step, followed by another, swaying left to right with each one. In this pitch-black place, he had to feel his way from floor to wall. Soon his outstretched hand found a cold, flat metal object. As his hand moved over it, he was certain it was a doorknob, and his one chance at freedom. When he turned it, the door sprang outward so quickly he almost lost his balance again as it slammed into a wall on his right.

Cringing with the crash and resulting vibration of the slamming door, he wondered if he was alone. As he lurched sideways again, he thought he must be on a ship. Though he'd never been on one before—just a dinghy on the pond back in Oak Grove when he was a child. So the only house he thought that could rock this much must be a ship, and a wooden one at that.

Book One of the Whimsy Tree Tales

Continuing cautiously forward, he stumbled onto a step. Trying not to make a sound, he raised his left foot, then felt with his right hand for another. After about seven steps he found a second door, but this one had a window, as he could feel the cool glass on the side of his face as he bumped into it. Sighing, he saw that the window appeared to do him little good--it was dark on the other side of it as well.

Carson stopped and counted to three before turning this knob even more gently than the first, and held onto it more firmly. Steadily pulling it back, he felt the welcome rush of fresh air toss his hair. Closing the door behind him as gently as he could, he looked around. The brightness of the waving stars overhead shadowed and shone over the deck, including a wide wooden plank leaning down toward what must be the shore.

He moved to the rail with a tilting motion, then held onto it a moment to steady himself as he looked down. The stars lit the water all around the plank except for the shore that the plank slid softly back and forth upon. Beyond the plank was what appeared to be dry land, with trees and shrubs similar in appearance to those along the estuary in Waters End—his newest hometown.

While deciding whether to leave the ship or not, he heard a voice call out to him from the bank below.

"Carson, is that you?" said the trine sprite Princess Danika urgently, and just loud enough for him to hear.

"Yes!" he called back, happy to have found her.

"Be careful coming down the plank. It's tilted and has no railing to hold onto," she answered. "And it has notches, so don't trip if you can help it."

Making his way down carefully, he spotted her glowing wings and long, wavy blond hair before he saw her face, and she was smiling as she rushed up to him and hugged him tightly around his knees.

"Where are we?" they both said at the same time.

Danika giggled as she pulled water weeds from her hair. Sobering, she said, "This place has the smell of the old country, though I have not been here in a long time. How did you find me?"

"I went back into the parlor at Ford's, Evan and I thought you were playing hide and seek with us, so I took the first floor and he the second and third. I did not find you anywhere else downstairs, so I walked into the parlor to look behind the furniture. As I looked up, a flash of light caught my eye, then bam! I was on my bum in a small, dark room, rocking slowly from side to side."

More serious now, Danika explained that the same thing had happened to her, but that she was studying the crystal. It looked familiar, and she couldn't place where she had seen it before. When she woke up, she was lying on the gangplank, didn't know it, and rolled off into the muddy water below.

Noticing her dampness for the first time, he laughed with her, then asked anxiously, "How could we be in the old country? And wasn't it mid-morning when we left Ford's?"

"I'm not sure," replied Danika. "Unless the crystal prism did it to both of us. Maybe we should wait here and see if anyone else comes, at least until it gets light enough for you to see better."

"Good plan," said Carson as he moved up the river bank a little farther from the water's edge and plopped himself down with his back against a wide tree trunk with soft, spongy bark.

Danika joined him. While looking up to the deep night sky, she delighted in pointing out Esther, the good luck morning star, shining brightly up above. They whispered for a while, wondering what could happen next until tired from their adventure, they fell asleep.

And as they slept, the masthead of the old wooden ship opened a tired eye and wondered if the boy was one of the children prophesized to return so long ago by the seers. Not knowing, the ship kept a lookout for them both, making sure no wild beasts ventured near while they slept.

To be continued....

AUTHOR'S NOTE

This book was begun in February of 2009 when life as I knew it underwent a series of dramatic changes. What I have learned from all the ups and downs I have been through since is to never give up on a dream. For me, that dream is to learn how to write and publish fantasy-fiction books.

So, here's to the first in a series. May I continue to learn and to grow my craft for years to come.

IN APPRECIATION

I find myself lucky enough to have many persons to thank. I have a wide circle of friends and cohorts that mean so much to me. Love is always the answer, and in that vein, let me begin my personal thanks.

Special thanks to my birth sisters, Wendy Hein and Bambi Dinsmore, who helped me begin this writer's journey in 2009 during a sisters' retreat to the wineries in Solvang, California, and who encouraged me always.

To my heart sister, Gail Anderson, who refused to let me get stuck on start.

To my sandbox chum, Melinda Rogers, who encouraged me from the beginning, and insisted that I read her the book as I was writing it.

To my hope sister, Toni Johnson, with whom I shared the most amazing dolphin adventure when a large black dolphin singled us out, then swam around us three times in Honeymoon Bay in the summer of 2010 near Dunedin, Florida.

To Kathie Dunn for sharing with me the hidden beauty of Yosemite National Park, and for naming Beezos, the wing snatcher.

To Kelli Bond who read this book in its infancy and encouraged me to keep going.

To my muse, John Luttrell, for there can be no story, no magic without music, and it is he and his music that also began this writer's journey.

To my fellow authors and FB friends, Paul de Throe, David Rhodes, and Michael Shorde for their continual 'I cans.' Especially, thank you Paul for reading parts of this book from the beginning and encouraging me through my own doubts too many times to count. You're one in a million.

To Eugene Chugunov (Wickard), my graphic artist. I found Eugene through

99Designs.com, and he is amazing. I highly recommend him and 99Designs.

And last but definitely not least, I must thank Ramy Vance, my fiction-writing coach, Shavonne Clark, my editor, and the staff of the Self-Publishing School. Without all of them, I would never have learned how to properly write, edit, and publish this book.

Made in the USA
Las Vegas, NV
26 September 2021